智 能 氣 功

Chi-Lel™ Qigong:

Body and Mind Method

Hou Hee Chan

Based on the teaching and writings by Dr. Pang Ming

Benefactor Press

Disclaimer

To reduce the risk of injury, consult your doctor before beginning this or any exercise program. The instructions and advice presented are in no way intended as a substitute for medical counseling. The author, the editors, Benefactor Press, producers, participants and distributors of this book are not liable for any inadvertent errors or for misinterpretation or misuse of information presented here. The author, the editors, Benefactor Press, producers, participants and distributors of this book disclaim any liability or loss in connection with exercise and advice herein.

Copyright 2002 by Hou Hee Chan
Published by Benefactor Press
PO Box 2097
Rocklin, CA 95677
www.chilel.com
Cover design by Eva Lew
Pictures by Hou Hee Chan

ISBN: 0-9637341-9-9
Printed in United States of America

Special thanks to Dr. Pang

Founder and Director of Huaxia Zhineng Qigong Center.

To find the right paths and get in the right doors, one needs verbal instructions. If one practices assiduously, Tao will be achieved automatically.

Taiji Classic

This book is dedicated to my aunt, Wai Lim Chan,
with love, respect and gratitude.

*   *   *

Acknowledgments

How can I thank so many individuals who helped and encouraged me during this project? Nancy Parker spent numerous hours editing my first draft. Yeeming Laoshi of China posed for the pictures. B. J. Kish Irvine, Ph.D. proofread the book. With the endless discussions and practice with my brother, Luke Chan, I gained much understanding of Dr. Pang's work. My colleagues, Jeng Laoshi and Chen Laoshi of China, not only shared with me their experience in teaching and the secret of their success, they also taught me the art of practice. This book never would have finished had it not been for the support and encouragement of my wife, Eva Lew, who edited the final draft.

Most of all, I am indebted to all my students. By teaching them, I gained many insights into the art of qigong. They are not only my students, they are my colleagues and teachers.

Please note that this book is based on the writings and teachings of Dr. Pang. It is not a direct translation of his work.

Contents

Introduction

For thousands of years, Qigong has been part of Chinese Culture. Qigong consists of two words—qi and gong. In Qigong exercise, qi means life energy: an invisible and formless substance that powers the functions of all life. Gong means practice. Together, Qigong means by practicing or cultivating qi daily, one can achieve and maintain health and harmony. Through the years, Qigong has developed into five schools (Taoist, Buddhist, Confucian, Martial Art, and Medical) and hundreds of forms. Each form has its own characteristics, purposes, requirements and techniques. The techniques were seldom shared among the schools. In order to maintain their individuality, mystical and religious elements were added into Qigong. Qigong was mainly practiced quietly within families and in religious temples.

Since early 1960's, Qigong has gone through a fundamental change. It has changed from an art practiced by a few people into a common exercise performed daily by millions. At the same time, claimed benefits and special abilities are under increased scrutiny from the medical and scientific fields. Under these conditions, most of the traditional Qigong schools have redesigned themselves to adapt to the new environment. As a result, a new generation of Qigong methods has emerged. Chi-Lel™ Qigong is one of them.

Chi-Lel™ Qigong was developed in the 1970s by Grandmaster Pang Ming, a physician trained in both traditional Chinese medicine and Western medicine. In the past few decades, Chi-Lel™ Qigong has grown from a practice involving just a handful of students to the number one Qigong in China with more than ten million practitioners. The theories of Chi-Lel™ Qigong are based on the traditional "man and nature are one" with the input and explanations of modern science. Its methods incorporate the essence of different schools of traditional Qigong. Its teaching and healing techniques are based on the revolutionary Chi-field concept.

This book is divided into two sections. Section one is a brief introduction to Chi-Lel™ Qigong, and section two is the methodology of the second level of Chi-Lel™ Qigong, the Body and Mind Method.

Section I:

A Brief Introduction to Chi-Lel™ Qigong

The Characteristics of Chi-Lel™ Qigong

Chi-Lel™ Qigong has a complete qi theory: Wan Yuan One Entity Theory

All things in the universe, visible or invisible, are the manifestations of qi. In other words, qi is the source of all matter that makes up the universe. Qi is formless and invisible. The appearance or disintegration of matter (birth, death, etc.) is the transmutation (concentration or dispersal) of qi. Qi exists in and permeates everything.

Wan Yuan One Entity Theory consists of three parts:

1. **The universe and nature are one entity**

   Within the entity, there are numerous levels of materials, which permeate and transmute each other. Through actions and interactions of these materials, billions of thing emerge to form the universe.

2. **Human body is one entity**

   A human being consists of Jing (body), Qi and Shen (mind). These three things are the manifestations or different stages of qi. Qi can concentrate to become physical body, or it can change into Shen. Qi also nourishes both Jing and Shen. In traditional Qigong and Chinese Medicine, a human being is lead by the Shen, centered in the internal organs, and connected through Qi and blood in the meridians to form a complete body and mind entity.

   In Chi-Lel™ Qigong, this entity is formed by merging the Jing, Qi and Shen. Jing is Wan Yuan Qi, a combination of external and internal qi, in physical form. It is the tool for all activities. Jing requires the nourishment of Qi and the instruction of Shen. Qi and Shen, however, merge into the physical body. Qi is Wan Yuan Qi in nonphysical form, it is the power source of activity. Qi is the medium between Jing and Shen. It is the formless and invisible matter that maintains body functions as one entity. Shen is Wan Yuan Qi in a special form-- brain activity. It controls all activity. Jing, Qi and Shen depend on and interact with one another to form one entity.

3. **Human and universe are one entity**

   Since qi is the building block for both human beings and nature, it forms one entity at the very basic level. The evolution from one life form to the

8

other is the product of interaction between nature and the life form. The human being is a part of nature's cycle of birth and death and is always interacting with nature. Normally, there are three ways human beings perform interaction with nature.

1) **Energy.** Nature constantly recycles energy. Vegetation absorbs inorganic materials to create food for animals, and the waste and corpses of animals in turn fertilize vegetation. Humans are part of this cycle.

2) **Information.** After we eat an apple, qi in our body breaks it down to semi-qi and absorbs it into the body. Once it is transmuted into our own qi and becomes part of us, characteristics of the apple will disappear, but some of the information it contains will remain. In other word, all materials in our body retain some of the information from nature.

3) **Transmuting qi.** Qi surrounds all solid material. The closer the qi is to the material, the denser the qi is. Material can also transmute and absorb external qi to become its own. The absorption and transmutation of qi can change the characteristic of the material, such as turning iron into rust. We can use our own qi to influence and change the environment. Through the constant exchange of qi between man and nature, the two form an entity.

Chi-Lel™ Qigong not only emphasizes cultivating our own internal qi within the body, it also stresses the importance of absorbing external qi, the qi in nature or universal qi, for our own use. Because the mind has the ability to activate qi in all parts of the body, we can collect universal qi and transform it into our own by opening and closing, concentrating and dispersing qi with our minds. Since internal qi carries the blueprint for biological and psychological health, body functions will be strengthened and illness will disappear once qi in the body becomes bountiful.

Chi-Lel™ Qigong has a complete system of methods

It consists of three stages and six levels.

The three stages are: External Wan Yuan, Internal Wan Yuan and Central Wan Yuan.

The six levels are:

1. Level I, Lift Chi Up and Pour Chi Down Method.

Level I belongs to External Wan Yuan.

2. Level II, Body and Mind Method.
3. Level III, Five Elements Method.
    Levels II and III belong to Internal Wan Yuan.

4. Level IV, Central Meridian Method.
5. Level V, Central Line Method.
6. Level VI, Back to the Tao Method.
    Levels IV to VI belong to Central Wan Yuan.

Normally, internal qi circulates among the membranes of the cells. The natural occurrence of exchanging qi with the universe is carried out through the skin. The purpose of level I is to strengthen this natural ability and to open up and maintain the channels between man and nature. In this method, we use mind intent to release the internal qi and absorb the universal or external qi. By absorbing abundant qi from nature, both quantity and quality of internal qi will increase. Since this exchange takes place in the skin and involves external qi, it is called External Wan Yuan.

The Body and Mind Method emphasizes the merging of the body and the mind. It mainly cultivates qi in the body. Traditionally, the human body is divided into five levels, skin, muscles, tendons, blood vessels, and bones. Body and Mind Method promotes qi penetration and permeation deep inside the body. Once qi in the main and collateral meridians merge as one, body functions will be strengthened and enhanced.

The Five Elements Method is designed to cultivate qi in the heart, liver, spleen, lungs and kidneys. In Traditional Chinese Medicine, these five organs are linked to emotional and mental activities. When qi in these organs becomes plentiful, emotional and mental activities will be balanced and harmonized. By practicing the Body and Mind Method and the Five Elements Method, the physical body qi and inner organs qi will merge as one to form the internal qi. This is called Internal Wan Yuan.

The Central Wan Yuan is designed to cultivate the qi in the Central Meridian. The Central Meridian is a special meridian connecting Baihui and Huiyin. It does not merge until we have cultivated enough qi. There are three steps in the Central Wan Yuan. The first step is to cultivate qi in the Central Meridian. The second is to cultivate the Central Line, the center of the Central Meridian. In the third step, man and nature finally become one.

Chi-Lel™ consists of many secrets from different schools of Qigong

In most arts (qigong, singing, dancing, etc.), the principles and the paths to achieve the goal are well defined. Through years of practice, most artists have some secret techniques that they treasure and would not easily share. Chi-Lel™ combines many secrets from Confucian, Taoist, Buddhist, Medical and Martial Arts Qigongs. Secrets are not necessarily the essence or the goal of a particular Qigong, but they are the shortcuts to the ultimate goal.

Teaching methods consist of Intuitive Transmission, Verbal Instruction, and Physical Demonstration

In ancient days, accomplished teachers taught their best students through intuitive transmission. They did not teach verbally. They only used their mind intent to communicate with the students. If the student was talented enough, he would receive the transmission. Of course, in reality, not many people are that talented.

Chi-Lel™ Qigong takes this concept one step farther. Instead of depending on the student's abilities, Chi-Lel™ Qigong developed the Chi-Field teaching method. In this method, the teacher synchronizes everyone's thinking to form a united field. When a chi field is formed, the power of intent will be increased by the factor of the number of people in the Chi field. The learning and healing effects will then be multiplied.

Another way to explain the Chi Field concept is this:

Field: Hundreds of people each with an unlighted candle enter a room and try to see their surroundings.
Forming the Chi Field: The teacher with a lighted candle lights up everyone's candle. Note: the teacher's light would not be diminished.
Chi Field: Everyone in the room can see better.

Verbal instructions and physical demonstrations are the main teaching methods employed to make sure the students are able to perform the forms. Verbal instructions focus on the purposes of the movements as well as the intention and relaxation of the mind. Physical demonstrations focus on the correct form and form modifications for physical limitations.

Specific mind activities are not used

Chi-Lel™ Qigong does not chase after emptiness nor after absolute tranquility. It also does not require specific mind activities. In the External Wan Yuan stage, the mind activity concentrates on following the intention of each movement. For example, in the Lift Chi Up and Pour Chi Down Method, when the hands push out, the mind intent opens and releases outward. When the hands pull in, the mind intent withdraws inward. The union of mind intent with physical movements activate and strengthen the ability to exchange qi with nature. In Internal and Central Wan Yuan stages, the mind activity concentrates on merging with the movements.

Human activities consist of two parts: mind activity and physical activity. When the mind and body are united as one, qi will be included inside. Traditionally, practicing Qigong requires total tranquility. Total tranquility has two meanings. One is that the mind does not have a single thought (emptiness); the other is that the mind activities are united as one (concentration).

In high-level practice, most Qigong schools require that the mind concentrates on the body. For example, Buddhist Qigong requires one to be in the meditative stage at all times. No matter what one is doing, whether walking, resting, eating, sleeping, etc., one should be concentrating on the body movement without any distracting thoughts. From the very beginning, Chi-Lel™ Qigong encourages concentration on the body not only during practice, but also during daily life. When picking up a glass of water, if we focus on the glass, then body and mind are not united; but if we focus on the movement of picking up the glass, the body and mind are united. When body and mind are united, qi will be united. Jing (body), Qi, and Shen (mind) will be cultivated. If we can pay attention to the body and mind all the time, we can improve our practice quickly and easily.

The Qi-Inducing Method is used to activate qi

The practice of Qigong uses different methods to activate and strengthen qi's ability to concentrate, disperse, and circulate. The method Chi-Lel™ Qigong uses is called Qi-Inducing Method. It consists of three techniques—mind, body and sound.

1. Mind-inducing qi

In the external Wan Yuan stage, Chi-Lel™ Qigong uses the Mind-Inducing Qi method to activate body qi and universal qi. Most traditional Qigong schools use a Mind-Leading Qi Method to activate qi. In the Mind-Leading Qi Method, the mind and qi unite as one; then, the

12

mind leads the qi through a fixed path to circulate in the body. In the Mind-Inducing Qi Method, the mind focuses on the destination, and then induces the qi to go in that direction.

Chi-Lel™ Qigong uses the Mind-Inducing Method because most people are not able to concentrate for a long period of time. The Mind-Leading Qi Method requires the mind to lead the qi to circulate along a fixed path. If the mind cannot concentrate or the path is wrong, then the qi will be in the wrong channel and unwanted things may happen. For example, while practicing the Microcosmic Orbit method, breathing activates qi in the lower Dantien until it is hot. This is called "ignite the fire". When the fire is cultivated up to a certain degree, mind intent unites with the qi, and then the mind leads the qi to circulate in the Governing and Conception Meridians. This is called "leave the qi, follow the meridians". During this process, if the mind cannot concentrate or is not able to follow the meridians, qi will be in the wrong channel. This is called "the fire out of control". Once qi is in the wrong channel, the Shen (mind) in the brain cannot be nourished and loses its abilities. As a result, the practitioner may not be able to control his physical movements. This is called "into the devil".

In the Mind-Inducing Qi Method, this problem is prevented by putting one's mind intent on the destination, and letting the qi find its own path to get there. It is analogous to meeting someone at the Empire State Building in New York City. Instead of giving the person a specific route to get there (he may get lost if there is a detour), you just tell him to meet you in the building. As long as he can see the building, he will not get lost.

Traditional Chinese Medicine and Qigong consider the rhythms of human activities to be "up and down" and "open and close." We can keep our balance with nature through "open and close", or by constantly exchanging qi with nature. In the Lift Chi Up and Pour Chi Down Method, our mind intent combines with body movements to induce and unite body qi with universal qi in nature. When our hands are doing the open and close movements, our mind intent is doing the movements at the same time. Following the opening and closing of the pores and pressure points, body qi will go out and universal qi will come in. When pushing outward, our mind intent travels far away into the blue sky inducing the qi to go outward. When pulling inward, our mind intent focuses in the body, inducing universal qi to come into the body. Through these movements, the natural ability of exchanging qi will be strengthened, and the relationship between man and nature will be improved.

2. Body-inducing qi

Body-inducing qi uses body movements to induce and activate qi in the meridians. In Martial Arts Qigong (Taiji, Bagua, etc.), this is described as "Shen (mind) is into the body; qi follows the body movement." It means that when the body moves, qi will follow. This technique is called the Body-Inducing Qi Method and is used in the second level, the Body and Mind Method. There are twelve main meridians in our body. Each one is connected to certain organs and body parts. When activity of a certain part of the body increases, it will activate and strengthen the corresponding meridian qi. As a result, the function of that part of the body will be strengthened. Since most meridians end at the fingertips and the toes, the Body and Mind Method emphasizes moving the tips of the limbs and the small joints. When this area moves, it activates the whole meridian, increasing and strengthening qi circulation.

3. Sound-inducing qi

In this technique, certain sounds are pronounced to vibrate the inner organs. Different sounds activate different qi. This technique is used in the Five Elements Method.

Chi-Lel™ Qigong belongs to the Open System

Traditionally, most of the Taoist and Buddhist Qigongs start out by confining the Jing, Qi and Shen within the body and then cultivating them until they become one. Once they form a unit, they open up and exchange qi with nature. Finally, man and nature become one. The open system that Chi-Lel™ uses is based on the experience of ancient masters and the needs of today's society. Open means: Qi open, Jing (body) open and Shen open.

1. Qi open. From the very beginning, Chi-Lel™ requires that Jing, Qi and Shen all open up. For example, Level I works on opening and releasing qi. Besides releasing internal qi and absorbing external qi, it also works on opening and releasing the mind. By practicing this method, we can connect internal and external qi and absorb the abundant qi in nature. Compared with the closed system which only cultivates internal qi, the open system utilizes more resources and achieves results faster.

2. Jing open. This means combining qigong with daily activities. The goal is to make qigong and daily routines inseparable.

3. Shen open. A person is a product of nature and society. The open system includes opening up to nature and to society and to becoming part of nature and society. Among Jing, Qi and Shen, the most impor-

14

tant is to open up Shen. Shen is the "central command" of human activities. By respecting the laws of nature and following the moral standard of society (cultivating virtue), we free ourselves from the mental stage of "ME" and become part of nature and society.

Chi-Lel™ considers virtue as the basic requirement of qi cultivation. During daily life, we should work on improving our moral character and temperament and try to be balanced and harmonized with nature. When in a quiet place, we should cultivate qi. When in chaotic situations, we should cultivate Shen. We should separate emotions from actions and maintain self-control. Although Shen-open is a high level cultivation in traditional Qigongs, it is a basic requirement in all levels of Chi-Lel™ .

In the open system, results are multiplied in group practice. In the Chi-Field, everyone's Shen and Qi are open. The body movements are uniform. Vibrations in the chi-field enhance the practice of each individual. The Chi-Field is a win-win situation, but it is only able to exist in an open system.

External Qi is used for healing others without harming one's self

Traditionally, emitting qi for healing involves using our own Dantien qi. Only when we cultivate qi up to a certain level and the Dantien qi is plentiful, can we emit qi to help others. Even with caution, we still may lose some of our own qi. In the closed system, practitioners are very careful in not to emit their Dantien qi. Letting go of Dantien qi would hinder improvement. In Chi-Lel™, we not only cultivate our own internal qi but also collect external qi for our own use. The technique we use to collect and concentrate external qi is Lift Chi Up and Pour Chi Down Method. Once the external or universal qi is collected, we pour it into our own body to strengthen the body and to eliminate illnesses. If we pour that qi into someone else, it is emitting external qi to heal others. Since this qi is qi from nature, not our Dantien qi, it would not affect our internal qi.

Qi reactions are very common

When we practice Chi-Lel™, our health will gradually improve from one level to another. During this process, the body will dispose of mental and physical impairments hindering this improvement. When this happens, we may experience discomfort in the corresponding part of the body. This is called Qi Reaction. It occurs in three common ways.

1. Detoxification reaction

The body needs to get rid of toxins when health begins to improve. If this happens in a fast and strong manner, toxins will be discharged in a physical way. The most common forms of discharge are diarrhea, increased sputum, vomiting, runny nose, fever, sweating, rashes, etc. The difference between detoxification reaction and physical illness is that you do not feel sick. When fever occurs as a reaction, for example, your mind is very clear. Before assuming that a serious physical symptom (for example, chest pain) is a detoxification reaction, seek medical consultation with a physician.

2. Qi-attacking-illness reaction

The section of the body with an illness may feel worse after practice. This is called the qi-attacking-illness reaction. When qi becomes stronger after practice, it begins to attack the illness. If it cannot get rid of the illness right away, discomfort may appear. This kind of reaction occurs primarily in people with a chronic illness. After illness exists for a long period of time, the body adjusts to it and becomes balanced in an abnormal way. When qi begins to win, functions in the diseased area become more normal. As a result, you are more sensitive to the illness and feel that the illness is getting worse.

Someone who has a bone spur in his neck, for example, feels pain when he moves his shoulder. A few years later, he learns to limit his arm movements. The bone spur is still there, but his shoulder does not hurt anymore. This creates an abnormal balance. The human body is connected by many meridians. Let us say that normally there are ten meridians that go through the shoulder. When the bone spur occurs, it blocks three of them. As a result, some areas would not be nourished by qi. If he still uses the same range of motions as before, qi would not be able to go through that area. The blockages will create pain. Over time, that area will lose some of its function, dulling the sensation of pain. With qigong practice and accumulation of qi, these three blocked meridians will begin to open up. The shoulder functions will improve, including the sensation of pain. So, before he can fully recover, he feels that the pain and discomfort are worse than before.

This kind of reaction is actually the indication of improvement. Sometimes, this reaction may occur even in the absence of symptoms because the disease has not yet manifested in the body. At other times, qi is eradicating old illnesses as part of a purifying process.

3. Improvement reaction

Even healthy people, when their health improves from one level to another, may encounter qi reactions. As with people with illnesses, the body has to eliminate toxins as health improves from one level to another. For example, if crude oil represents a person with illness, kerosene a healthy person, and gasoline a healthier person, then going from one stage to the next, from crude oil to gasoline, a lot of unwanted materials need to be removed.

Qi reactions occur in all qigong practices. The reason they happen more often in Chi-Lel™ is because qi works so quickly in Chi-Lel™ that the body has to get rid of the toxins in a physical way.

The Difference Between Chi-Lel™ Qigong and other Qigong

Chi-Lel™ Qigong begins with merging with nature

Traditionally, most of the Taoist and Buddhist Qigongs start out by confining the Jing, Qi and Shen within the body and cultivating them until they become one. Once they form a unit, they then open up and exchange qi with nature. The cultivate method is from inside out. Chi-Lel™ Qigong uses the opposite approach. It begins with merging internal qi with nature qi. In level I, this merging and exchanging of qi occur in the skin. In level II and level III, this exchange will occur in the Meridian, inner organs, Center Meridian and Center line. Qi gradually permeates inward until man and nature are one.

Chi-Lel™ Qigong does not focus on Meridians nor Orbit practice

In Chi-Lel™ Qigong, meridians and orbits practices are mentioned but not practiced. Meridian and orbit practice use mind intent to activate and move qi in the meridians, following the paths of Microcosmic and Macrocosmic orbits to increase qi abilities and movement. Instead, Chi-Lel™ Qigong focuses on strengthening the ability of lateral meridians to merge qi into one entity. To illustrate this difference, irrigation can be done by irrigation ditches or by flooding the field. In the ditch method, water (qi) from the ditches (meridians) irrigate the field (body). Qi circulation in the meridian is very important. In flooding the field method, the field (body) completely floods with water (qi). The role of the ditches (meridians) is not that important.

Chi-Lel™ Qigong emphasizes Moving Forms

Most qigong methods emphasize Stillness Forms (standing or sitting). They consider Moving Forms as elemental and Stillness Forms as advanced. In truth, both can be elemental or advanced. The reasons why Chi-Lel™ Qigong emphasizes the moving form are:

1. Stillness forms require that the mind be in an emptiness stage (devoid of thought or stimulation). Taoist Qigong requires no mind

activities, no breathing, no blood circulating. Buddhist Qigong requires the mind to become a mirror, reflecting what comes in without any comment. This is very difficult, if not impossible, to achieve. Only when all meridians open up can the mind calm down. For example, if one does the double-Lotus sitting qigong before he is ready, he would not be able to let go of his mind nor be able to sit very long. The numbness and pain in the legs will occupy his mind, and results will not be achieved. Chi-Lel™ Qigong concentrates on opening up the meridians and using the moving forms to strengthen the circulation of qi.

2. In order to attain better health, not only do the meridians have to be open and qi be abundant, but the volume of qi circulating in the body has to be increased. There are two ways to increase qi volume. One way is to strengthen existing channels, and the other is to open up new channels. Moving forms both strengthen existing channels and open up new channels.

3. In the advanced level, the distracted mind and the non-distracted mind, are cultivated. Practicing alone in a closed room cultivates the non-distracted mind. Maintaining inner peace while mingling with the chaos of the real world cultivates the distracted mind. Cultivation of the non-distracted mind only is still elemental practice. Moving forms and group practice Chi-Lel™ are easy ways to concentrate and work on the distracted mind.

Chi-Lel™ Qigong emphasizes group practice

Traditionally, most people practice qigong in isolation in order to achieve an undisturbed mind. Accomplished practitioners spend years in the mountains or temples alone. In today's society, this is very difficult if not impossible to do. Even at home, with minimum distraction, we have difficulty maintaining a regular practice. Once the Chi-Field is formed in group practice, learning abilities and healing effect will be enhanced. Maintaining focus is much easier to achieve with group strength and support.

How to Practice Chi-Lel™ Qigong

Purpose and Affirmation

Whether we practice qigong for health or enlightenment, we must have a purpose and firmly believe that we can achieve the ultimate goal. A strong belief can be transformed into will power that overcomes mental and physical difficulties. This belief consists of two parts.

1. Believe and trust that Chi-Lel™ can lead us to our goal

There are thousands of qigong methods, all claiming to be the best. Although the grass always looks greener on the other side of the fence, we must take a close look at the records. Hundreds of thousands of people have achieved their goals by practicing Chi-Lel™ in the U.S. and China through the years. Scientific studies performed in China have demonstrated its effectiveness in healing illnesses. As long as we continue to practice Chi-Lel™, it will improve our health.

2. Believe and trust it can be done

Sometimes people give up hope when doctors tell them they have incurable diseases. Medicine is just a small part of the total health system. When doctors say a disease is incurable, it does not mean that it is incurable in all other ways. Diseases come and go, but man is still around. We have the capability to heal ourselves. In qigong, no two persons are alike in the time and effort needed to achieve results. Thus, it is very important not to give up when results are not evident after a period of practice. The mills of qi grind slowly, but they grind mighty fine. Results can be achieved if belief is combined with effort and persistence.

Respect

Respecting the Tao and the teacher is a fundamental principle of qigong. Tao is nature. To respect nature is to respect the environment and all living things. Only by respecting nature can we become part of nature. When we become part of nature, we will receive information and vitality from nature.

In qigong, Tao also encompasses methodology, purpose and virtue. To practice qigong is to cultivate Tao. By working on techniques alone, we can only achieve perfection of our skills. By working on techniques, following the principles, and having virtue, we can then cultivate Tao. One of the principles in Chi-Lel™ is living in a state of complete physical, mental, and social well-being. When we have mental or physical setbacks, we need to address the issues instead of blaming others or becoming dejected and giving up. By believing in ourselves, we can face challenges and receive satisfaction in overcoming them. This is respecting the Tao of Chi-Lel™.

To respect the Tao of a certain qigong we should practice that qigong wholeheartedly. We should be very careful in choosing the kind of qigong to practice. Some qigongs may not be worthy of respect. For example, some qigongs say that there are three thousand six hundred side doors and eighty four thousand side roads and they are the only path leading one to the Tao. How do we know what is the right path? What is the standard for comparison? In Chi-Lel™ perspective, the good qigong improves physical and mental health without interfering with other's well-being; otherwise, the qigong is not good. On an individual basis, a good qigong is one that can helps the individual achieve his or her goal.

Can we practice different kinds of qigong at the same time? Each qigong has its own characteristics, purposes, requirements and techniques which will create a certain rhythm in the body with practice. If more than one qigong is practiced, the rhythms produced by one may interfere with another. Chaos may occur. This may also hamper improvement. One may reach water a lot faster by digging one well instead of ten. Committing to one qigong is respecting the Tao.

Confucius once said, "Among three persons, one can be my teacher." What is a teacher? A teacher is anyone who can help us make progress toward our goal. If someone has expertise in one area, learn from him. If another person makes a mistake, learn from his experience, and avoid the same mistake. Time is limited, so we should tap into the vast resources of fellow practitioners.

As a teacher, we should not take respect as a given right. A teacher must earn the respect from his students. We should always ask ourselves "Am I good enough to be a teacher?" Good includes two parts. One is proficiency. Does we practice and know the methods well enough to teach? A teacher must walk the walk before talking the talk. The other is virtue. Do we teach for the good of the students or for the good of ourselves? It is unethical to withhold secrets and mislead students. To respect others is to respect ourselves.

Ardor

Whether we achieve the Tao or not depends entirely on ourselves. Tao comes from within and cannot be taught. The methods may be excellent and the teacher may share all secrets, but if we do not practice, they are useless. The methods are the gates and paths leading to the Tao. Teachers can point out the correct gates and paths to take, but we still have to walk down the road. How?

1. Be assiduous and persevering

Once the gates and paths are identified, we must follow them carefully. In other words, we must follow the mental and physical requirements of the method. We need to know the purposes and functions of the movements and practice them assiduously and perseveringly. Only through time can results be accomplished and the Tao be achieved. As they say in United States, the only way to Carnegie Hall is by practice, practice and practice.

How much and how hard should we practice? Everyone is different. Mental and physical conditions needs to be considered. A practice schedule should be a regular part of the daily routine like brushing the teeth. Practice up to maximum ability, but do not be obsessed. Do not compare with others; only with ourselves. Find out what makes the improvements or setbacks. There is always room for growth. Results take time and effort to obtain. Once the schedule is set, stay with it. Never practice to a point where it takes a few days for the body to recover. This will harm the body. Listen to the body. Know when to stop. When the body is getting better, discomfort may appear. Stay with the practice; otherwise, we may go backward. Be patient. Rome was not built in one day.

2. Progress gradually

Qigong practice is like a thousand-mile journey; we have to take it one step at a time. To get results, persistence and determination are needed. Everything happens in its own time. Being too eager for success, like pulling the seedling up to help it to grow, is harmful. The rule of thumb is progress gradually, from simple to complex and from one to many. After a proper practice, we should feel that the body is rejuvenated, the mind is relaxed, and we are harmonized with nature.

One of the common mistakes made by many practitioners is to consider learning new forms progress. As we will discuss later, there are many levels of practice within one form. It is not how many forms we know, it is how well we know them. Every trail leads to the mountain top. Just do it, one practice at a time. As long as we follow the principles, we will arrive at the goal.

Relaxation, Quietness and Being Natural

Relaxation

Relaxation consists of two parts, physical and mental.

Physical requirement in Chi-Lel™ is that the body is relaxed but not collapsing, poised but not stiff. We use qi not force. Body postures are poised, and maintain a certain degree of tension without being stiff. The perfect example for achieving this requirement is when a baby reaches for something. The baby's natural body posture is what we call "relaxing without collapsing."

One of the most common misconceptions about relaxing is to "not use any force". To maintain our body posture without collapsing, we need to have some force. "Not using any force" in this case means using unnecessary force. If maintaining body posture takes ten pounds of force, then using ten pounds is not using force; using 10.1 pounds, however, is using force and 9.9 pounds is collapsing.

How can we maintain this kind of relaxation? When the physical body begins to relax, the mind intent has to expand. As the mind expands through the body, the trapped force or excess tension will be released. Qi follows the mind. In the moving qigongs such as Body and Mind Method and internal martial arts, the mind has to penetrate into every movement. Whether qi is present or not will depend on the penetration and expansion of the mind. When the mind is excited, it is very difficult to have a relaxed body.

One of the most effective relaxing methods is called the Three-Line Relaxation Method or the Sections Relaxation Method. In Chi-Lel™, we use the Sections Relaxation Method for preparation most of the time. Students follow the teacher's instructions to relax each section of the body, from head to toes, and then continue by expanding the mind (head touches sky, feet stand on earth, etc..) Sometimes, we combine Sections Relaxation Method with the Sound Vibrating Method. For example, when the teacher says, "relax the head," students concentrate on the head, mentally relax it, and at the same time pronounce "Sown."

Quietness

Normally, quietness refers to the mind in a tranquil state. Quietness has two meanings. One is that the mind does not have a single thought; the other is that the mind concentrates on one thing only -- a thousand thoughts are substituted with one. It is not easy to maintain a single thought without any interruption for a long period of time (i.e., forty-five minutes), let alone not having one single thought. The quietness Chi-Lel™ is looking for can be found in concentrating on doing the movements without distractions. In the Three Centers Merge Standing Method, one of the techniques for concentrating is to keep repeating "three centers are merging into the Dantien". If we can repeat that for a hundred times without distractions, we achieve the requirement of quietness.

Be Natural

This refers to following the natural rhythms of our own body. Nothing is forced.

The aim of practicing qigong is to purify body movements, to strengthen beneficial ones, and to eliminate harmful ones. In the beginning, qigong requirements seem awkward. Awkwardness does not mean unnatural. We have acquired numerous bad habits over the years that strengthen some abilities and weakened others. This imbalance can harm the body. Many movements in Chi-Lel™ are designed to correct habitual movements.

Going back to the natural uninhibited stage may cause an unnatural feeling in the beginning. Everyone starts from a different point. What is natural for one person may not be natural for another. We should listen to our own bodies and find the most comfortable way to practice. When we believe we are practicing to the best of our abilities, our minds will relax and be natural. For example, if someone has limited mobility in the upper body and can only perform half of a movement in the prescribed way, as long as he respects his body's limitations, he has met the requirement to be natural. Visualizing a non-moving part moving can lead qi through that area, causing illness to gradually disappear. If someone always shows off in front of others, he will not be able to consolidate qi.

Qigong is an inward cultivation. We should not compare ourselves with others, especially the disadvantaged ones. If we do not feel comfortable with our own practice and fear other people watching us, we are not being natural. As a matter of fact, no one pays attention to the others in a group practice. Once the eyes are closed, each person is the only person in the world. Everything around him does not exist anymore. He and nature have become one. Accepting our limitations and working hard to improve them is what being natural is all about.

Nourishment

Qigong requires two things, practice and nourishment.

Nourishment includes good nutrition and adequate rest. When health improves from one level to another, the demand for qi in quantity and quality greatly increases. During this time, we may feel tired and drained. The reason is that once new channels for qi open up, we do not have enough qi to fill them. Only when we accumulate enough qi will that feeling disappear. For example, assume the volume in each level is ten liters. When level one begins to fill up, we feel very energized and have plenty of qi. But once channels open up between level one and level two, the combined volume is twenty liters and we still have only ten liters of qi. So the pressure drops. We may feel tired and has less energy. It is not a sign of regression, but an indication of improvement. During this stage, practice and nourishment are very important. We should continue to practice hard and have plenty of rest and proper nutrition.

Chi-Lel™ recommends a balanced diet with dietary supplements, if necessary. In order to survive in adverse conditions, wild animals and plants absorb and retain vast amounts of universal qi. So "wild" food (animals, vegetables, fruits, etc.) is better than farm raised; organic food is better than regular food, fresh food is better than canned food. When choosing food, select a variety of sources and flavors. According to Traditional Chinese Medicine, different flavors and foods nourish different inner organs. For example, foods with sour flavor nourish the liver. Wheat, onions, lamb and almonds nourish the heart. Too much or too little of one food can lead to illness.

In the qigong methods, traditional moving qigong is considered practice, while stillness qigong is considered nourishment. Chi-Lel™ incorporates practice and nourishment into the movements. In Chi-Lel™, nourishment means qi circulating uninterrupted. We get sick when qi is blocked in one area of the body, depriving the area of proper qi nourishment. No matter how much rest and nutrition we get, as long as qi is blocked, illness remains. Only by opening all the meridians can the body then get the proper nourishment.

From the very beginning, the goal of Chi-Lel™ practice is to merge ourselves and nature into one, to facilitate releasing internal qi and absorbing external qi. When we use mind intent to activate qi, it is practice; when we absorb universal qi into the body, it is nourishment. Each open and close sequence contains one practice and one nourishment. We consider Lift Chi Up and Pour Chi Down Method as practice and Three Centers Merge Standing Method as nourishment. In contrast, Body and Mind Method is practice, and the Lift Chi Up and Pour Chi Down Method is nourishment.

Chi-Lel™ considers practice and nourishment as one, different, yet inseparable. Generally speaking, open and release movements are practice, and close and absorb movements are nourishment. On a deeper level, the process of closing is practice, and the split-second before opening is nourishment. Breathing in and out is considered practice, while the pause between inhaling and exhaling is nourishment. A bow with too much tension becomes rigid; with too little tension it becomes slack. In either case, the bow is useless. Only when the proper degree of tension exists will the bow become useful. If we understand this principle, then we will find that every qigong method has both practice and nourishment. When practice is combined with nourishment, health improves quickly.

Time and Place

We need to work out a schedule according to our own circumstances. Ideally, we should practice at the same place, same time and for the same length of time every day. Do not be too ambitious; be realistic. Once the schedule is set, stay with it. When we feel sick, stay with the practice. This is the time when we need qi the most. After a long day at work, practice can rejuvenate our tired body and mind. We can overcome lots of temptations and excuses to quit by staying with a realistic schedule.

Practicing qigong not only cultivates the qi, but more importantly, cultivates the mind. If we continue to practice in adverse circumstances, we can increase our mental abilities to deal with mundane daily activities. It is also habit forming. By practicing at the same place, a qi field is created by attracting qi into that room every day. After awhile, we may notice our small pets coming in and sitting around while we practice. They are attracted to the strong qi in the area. If our minds remain relaxed, these animals may actually protect the chi field.

In order to advance to higher levels, practicing only in a fixed time and place is not enough. We need to incorporate qigong into daily life and practice all day long. There are two ways to practice. One is to practice in a set place, at a set time and with set routines. This is called doing a "gong". The other is to apply qigong principles into daily activities. For example, before picking up a book to read, close the eyes for a few seconds and concentrate on the lower Dantien. When reading, continue to pay attention to the lower Dantien. By connecting the Dantien with every movement, we are practicing qigong. We should also move with the proper body postures at all times, not just during practice. While walking, suspend the head from above, relax the shoulders, drop the elbows, push the Mingmen out, relax the whole body, and pay attention to the Dantien. This is walking qigong. Recall that qigong requires the mind to be calm and relaxed. The best way to train is by applying qigong principles to the chaos of daily life. If we can remain calm and centered during adverse circumstances, we are practicing the highest level of qigong.

One of the key points in qigong is to merge mental with physical activities; perform every movement mindfully. For example, to erect the palms: first, the brain thinks of erecting the palms (mental activity); then, it issues the command to erect the palms. Then the body begins to move (physical activity), and the palms are erected. When the mind is concentrated on the movement of erecting the palms, it is merging mental activity with physical activity. Qigong practice is flexible. Routine work can be very boring, sometimes becoming a hazard. If we can put our minds into the routine and be conscious of our body movements all the time, we are practicing qigong.

Different Ways to Practice Qigong

Traditionally, qigong practice is divided into three major ways

1. Jing Practice

In this practice, the focus is on strengthening the abilities of the physical body. Qi and Shen service Jing or body posture. Although Shen plays a vital role in this, it is not the focal point. By strengthening Jing, Qi and Shen will be strengthened as well. Most martial art qigongs uses this approach.

2. Qi Practice

The focus is on Qi, and Jing and Shen service Qi. Again, Shen plays a vital role in this, but it is not the focal point. One of the major branches of Taoist qigong, Dan Tao Qigong, uses this approach.

3. Shen Practice

The focus is on Shen. Jing and Qi service Shen. The Zen branch of Buddhist Qigong uses this approach.

Although focal points are different, these practices overlap one another. It cannot be said that Jing practice is pure Jing nor that Qi is pure Qi. Chi-Lel™ Qigong uses two approaches. One is Shen and Qi practice and the other is Shen and Jing practice.

Shen and Qi Practice

The main characteristic of this practice is that Shen and Qi complement one another; they use and help each other. There are four steps to this practice.

a. Shen Thinking Qi

Qi is a unique substance that is formless and invisible in normal circumstances. This practice requires the mind to integrate with this unique substance. After a period of practice, we will begin to feel the existence of qi. Two kinds of qi are present in this practice; external qi and internal qi. In the beginning, Chi-Lel™ Qigong concentrates on joining the mind with external qi. The purpose of thinking blue sky in the level 1 practice is to connect the mind with Wan Yuan Qi or primordial qi. One important point is that the blue sky is not empty but filled with formless, odorless, colorless qi. Normally, this substance is very difficult to feel. The feeling of qi that we experience while practicing comes from internal qi scattered around the body.

b. Shen Observing Qi

Observation means to feel and to see. When Shen observes qi, it means seeing qi or feeling qi. When seeing qi we can see either internal qi or external qi. The qi we see while doing La Chi is external qi. Observing the internal qi is more difficult, requiring proficiency in observing external qi first. Different kinds of qi (organ qi, meridians qi, etc.) interact with one another inside the physical body. These compartments of qi are affected not only by the changes in the physical body, but also by the mind's activities. Through tranquil observation, we can feel a hazy qi being. One sensation is the qi being engulfs the body. This occurs when we feel and see the internal qi scattered around our own body. The other sensation is the qi being is inside the body. This occurs when we feel and see the qi in the cell membranes.

c. Shen into Qi

In Shen observes Qi, Shen is the observer and Qi is the target. They are separate. This practice requires that Shen get inside Qi. How do we achieve this? When we are able to observe qi accurately, we begin to see it in detail from head to toe. Shen will automatically go into Qi with repetition of this process. The key is supreme concentration and continual observation.

d. Shen and Qi become one

In the Shen into Qi stage, Shen and Qi are still separate. In this stage, Qi is cultivated to a point where it becomes Shen. How does this happen? While observing internal and external qi, Shen expands, engulfs and permeates Qi. Shen and Qi then become one.

Shen and Posture Practice

The main characteristic of this practice is that the Shen and body postures complement each other; they use and help each other. There are three steps for this practice.

a. Shen Thinking Posture Stage

In this stage, mind activities are integrated with the body movements. Mind activates and directs every body movements. This seems very simple, yet it is not easy to do. If the mind cannot concentrate or wanders slightly, it fails the requirement of Shen thinking posture. Once we master this stage, distracting thoughts will cease to exist.

b. Shen Observing Postures Stage

In this stage, Shen is seeing or feeling the body movements. It can be divided into two steps.

(a). Shen observing external body postures. With the eyes closed during practice, Shen is "observing" our own body movements as if watching someone else practicing. Shen can be observing movements from the front of the body. Shen can also look into the Dantien area to observe a small self doing the practice. Once Shen is able to observe the whole sequence of movements, the mind has achieved a high level of self-control.

(b). Shen observing internal body postures. Once we have achieved certain proficiency in observing external body postures, Shen's abilities to observe and penetrate will allow us to see through the body. For example, Shen can see and feel the movement of qi inside the body when the body moves. With practice, we can see the circulation of qi inside our bodies and the exchange of qi between ourselves and nature. One important point is that we can only observe, not analyze. In traditional qigongs, this is called "tranquility and reflection." Tranquility means that the mind is calm. Reflection means that the mind only observes and reflects changes in the body like a reflecting pond — the calmer the water, the better the reflection.

c.   Shen into Body Posture Stage

While observing the internal body, Shen fixes on a particular point and observes the surrounding areas from that point. When this is achieved, Shen is into the body.

The reason for dividing Shen and Qi practice and Shen and Body practice into different stages is for better understanding. In actual practice, the stages overlap one another. Shen and Qi practice and Shen and Body practice also overlap one another. The point of focus differentiates the stage and the practice.

Section II:

The Methods

We mold clay into a pot, but it is the emptiness inside that makes it useful.

Tao Te Ching

Part 1:
The Body & Mind Method

Introduction

The Body & Mind Method (Shing Shen Chong) is a special name for the second level of Chi-Lel™ Qigong. In Chinese, Shing means "physical body", Shen means "mind activities", Chong means "body postures". Together, the title means to practice Jing (Shing), Qi and Shen postures. This method uses "Shen merges into Shing" and "Shing follows Shen" techniques to achieve Shing-Shen merging as one entity. This is called Shing Shen Wan Yuan.

At the beginning stage of Shing Shen Wan Yuan, mind and body activities merge as one. Although body movements are directed by mind intent, the mind intent is not focused on the body movement but on the destination of the movement. This is outward-mind-intent.

The Body & Mind Method requires the Shen to fully concentrate on the body area performing the movement, and gradually penetrate into the muscles, tendons and bones. Because qi follows Shen, qi will permeate inside the muscles, tendons, and bones. On the cellular level, qi which is usually concentrated in the membranes will follow Shen into the cell. When internal qi increases to a point where intracellular qi and membrane qi become one, it is called internal Shing Shen Wan Yuan.

"Shen concentrates in Chong, Qi follows Chong's movement" is the basic principle of traditional moving qigongs. Body & Mind Method uses this principle in "Shen and Posture Practice", which requires Shen to concentrate on the body posture. This belongs to "Shen thinking posture stage". If we have a solid foundation in cultivating external Wan Yuan qi, we may feel qi in the section of the body we are working on. As we move into "Shen Observing Postures Stage", we will begin to feel and observe the conditions around the body part actively involved in practice.

Characteristics of the Body & Mind Method

High Degree of Difficulty

Movements in the Body and Mind Method are based on Martial Art Qigongs and Traditional Moving Qigongs. It consists of ten sections, which can be practiced individually. The movements, which are mostly straight or square with a few circular movements, are very simple. Since the method is designed to correct body postures and imbalance of Qi caused by daily life, its movements may feel awkward compared to habitual movements. It also exercises areas such as small joints and back muscles that are ignored during daily routines. At the beginning, if we practice the form correctly, we may feel that the movements are unnatural; our bodies may feel sore and tired.

Movements are Balanced

Body & Mind Method emphasizes body movement, and is sturctured to move every part of the body. It is divided into three sections:

Body—head, neck, chest, back, ribs, stomach, hip bone, and tail bone.
Upper limbs—shoulder, elbow, wrist, palm, and fingers.
Lower limbs—hip joint, knee, ankle, feet, and toes.

The movements balance left and right, front and back, and up and down. They work on extension and contraction of muscles and tendons and mobility and flexibility of the joints. Following mind intent, we exercise almost every part of the body. Practicing this method will balance Qi and beautify the body.

Use Posture Inducing Qi Method

In general, each body movement consists of two kinds of Qi Inducing Method-- fast and slow. When a command is given to execute a certain movement, the mind focuses on the areas involved in the movement. At the same time, Wan Yuan Qi (the merged external and internal Qi) concentrates in that area. This process is called "intent arrives, Qi arrives". This is a fast process, occurring in a split second. As the body moves and posture changes, Meridian Qi activates and alters its distribution. Meridian Qi circulates to its own rhythms, which is subjected to the influence of body movements and internal organ activities. Consequently, Meridian Qi in the moving areas will increase. This is a slow process. Body movement and Meridian Qi movement work together to maintain body vitality.

The Body and Mind Method activates qi by the following process. "Mind intent induces Qi; Qi induces body postures; postures induce Qi; Qi activates the mind." Mind intent induces Qi to concentrate on a target area; the merging intent and Qi produce body movements. The movements activate Meridian Qi and cause qi and blood in the moving area to concentrate, expand, and circulate. The expansion attracts the mind's attention, and consequently, Wan Yuan Qi follows the mind's attention and concentrates in the area.

Activates Meridian Functions

According to Meridian theory, all internal organs and limbs are connected through the meridian channels. Each meridian contains qi circulating in distinctly characteristic fashion and connects with one another at different parts of the body. For example, hands and fingers are connecting points for Hand Yin Meridians and Hand Yang Meridians; head is the connecting point for Hand Yang Meridians and Foot Yang Meridians; feet are the connecting points for Foot Yin Meridians and Foot Yang Meridians; chest and stomach are the connecting point for Foot Yin Meridians and Hand Yin Meridians. Because the human body needs to exchange qi with the nature constantly, and external qi enters the body mainly through the tips of hands and feet, meridian theory consider tips of limbs the roots of meridians. Meridians end in the head and internal organs.

Following the meridian principles, Body & Mind Method emphasizes exercising the limbs. In Section I, the focus is on the head. Once the head moves, limbs will follow, and qi will be activated. Section II & III work on the hands; section VII, VIII and IX work on the lower limbs.

Shing & Shen as One, Use both Tension & Relaxation

Due to a high degree of complexity, it is very difficult to practice Body & Mind Method as required without using force at the beginning. Once force is used, it is very easy to become rigid and tense, which violates the principles of relaxation and flexibility. To resolve this conflict, Body & Mind Method use both tension and relaxation.

1. At the beginning, do not be afraid to use force. The first priority is to obtain the proper posture. Only when we learn the new routine can we

begin to relax. When tension appears in the body, use mind intent to relax it. When the body is tense and the mind is relaxed while maintaining the correct posture, it is call "Shing is tense, Shen is relaxed".

2. Parts of the body are tense; the rest of the body is relaxed. During the practice, the moving area exerts a certain degree of tension to obtain the proper posture, while the non-moving part is totally relaxed. Tension is not brute force or unnecessary force, it is the right amount of strength required to perform the movement. Once we develop internal strength, we will automatically become relaxed.

Angular outside, circular inside

The Body & Mind Method contains numerous straight and angular movements. When changing from one posture to another, angles are very obvious. Although this kind of movement is very effective in activating meridian qi, it lacks finesse and smoothness. It also contradicts the principle of "circular and flexible." In practice, the Body & Mind Method uses two techniques to solve this problem.

1. **Angular outside, circular inside:** For example, in bending the elbows movement, the elbows form a very obvious 90-degree angle outside (between the upper arm and forearm). In the inner side of the angle, however, the mind intent forms an outward expanding circular force. This outward expanding circular force creates the "angular outside, circular inside" posture.

2. **Use both straightened and bent movements:** The movements are straight, yet not straightened to the limit. The joints are relaxed to maintain their flexibility and to prevent over extension.

Contains both large and small movements

The Body & Mind Method exercises every section of the body. It contains both large and small movements. For example, section VI, Bend Body, Arch spine and Loosen Governing Meridians and section XI, Wan Yuan and Qi Return to One, are large movements. Section IV, Erect Palms, Separate Fingers and Open Meridians, are small movements. In addition, each section consists of large and small movements. For example, shoulder, elbow, and knee movements are large; wrist, finger, ankle and toe movements are small. Waist movement is large; vertebrae movement is small, etc. General speaking, the body movements that can be easily observed are considered large; the internal movements, which are more difficult to be observed, are considered small. The reason why the Body & Mind Method consists of both large and small movements are two fold.

1. In daily routines and exercises, most people have a tendency to focus on large movements and neglect small ones. The Body & Mind Method specifically corrects this mistake. Small movements require agility and precision. Focusing on them develops a high degree of concentration. Consequently, quietness can be achieved.

2. Small movements are very effective in activating meridians to improve the circulation of qi and blood.

The Form

Preparation

Stand straight with the inner sides of both feet slightly touching each other.
The body is centered, and the hands relaxed naturally with the fingers pointing
to the ground. The knees and arms are straight but not locked. Look at the
horizon; then slowly withdraw vision inward and gently close eyelids. The
whole body is relaxed. To relax and balance the body, shift weight to the balls
of feet, use Baihui to lead the body to rock back and forth slightly a few times.
Fig. 1-1.

Fig 1-1

A. Physical Posture

1. **Head:** As if suspended by a string from Baihui, the head remains re-laxed and centered at all times. The chin is tucked in (the nose seeking Huiyin will achieve that). The line connecting the eyebrows is always parallel to the ground. The eyes are relaxed, and the vision is with-drawn inward. The mouth is closed with the lips gently touching each other. The tip of the tongue touches the upper palate between the upper teeth and the gum. The upper and lower front teeth touch each other.

   Purpose: The head plays a vital role in centering the body. If the head is not centered, the body will not be able to achieve the proper posture. A centered head induces qi upward to nourish the brain. If the head leans backward, qi in the Governing Meridian will have difficulty in moving upward, causing numbness in the neck area. If the chin does not tuck in, qi in the Conception Meridian will not be able to move downward easily, resulting in dizziness and high blood pressure. The reason for the tongue touching the upper palate is to reconnect the Conception Meridian so that qi can move from the Governing Meridian to the Conception Meridian and complete the circle.

2. **Neck:** The neck should be relaxed and straight with the Adam's apple withdrawn inward and upward toward Yuzheng.

   Purpose: A relaxed and straight neck induces Qingyang qi upward to nourish the brain. If the Adam's apple is not withdrawn inward, qi in the chest area will not be able to go downward.

3. **Upper limbs:** All joints are naturally relaxed and loose. Elbows should be straight but not locked; wrists sit downward; palms are cupped as if they are holding balloons; fingers are naturally extended.

   Purpose: There are six meridians in the upper limbs. Loose joints allow qi to go through and nourish the limbs.

4. **Shoulder:** The shoulder joints are relaxed and naturally hanging loosely. Upper arms are turned outward and inward slightly to create an empty space in the underarm area.

   Purpose: If the upper arm touches the rib area, it will create a block-age in the shoulder joint to prevent qi from flowing to the fingertips. The space in the underarm area prevents that from happening,

5. **Chest:** The chest is expanded and relaxed. The triangle area formed by the nipples and throat is withdrawn slightly inward. At the same time, chest expands outward from both sides.

   Purpose: Expanding the chest expands the lung capacity and allows qi to go downward. The chest area is the junction point for the six Yin Meridians. Relaxing the chest and pulling up the thoracic vertebrae maintains the smooth connections between the Yin Meridians, which connect the inner organs, to ensure their normal function.

6. **Back:** The vertebrae are straightened by pulling up from the first thoracic vertebra while the tailbone is pulling down toward the ground.

   Purpose: Loosening up the vertebrae creates an easy path for qi to go upward along the Governing Meridian.

7. **Abdomen and Waist:** Withdraw the abdomen by moving the navel toward the Mingmen, and at the same time pulling up Huiyin. The waist is relaxed with the 2nd, 3rd and 4th lumbar vertebrae protruding backward. Tailbone is pointing to the ground. Hip joints are relaxed.

   Purpose: Withdrawing the abdomen helps the process of absorbing qi into the kidneys. The lumbar vertebrae protruding backward enlarge the Dantien Area. This area can then not only store more qi and better regulate qi flow in the body, but improve absorption of qi in the kidneys as well.

8. **Lower Limbs:** All joints are naturally relaxed and loosened. Knees are straight but not locked and are turned slightly inward.

   Purpose: Loose joints allow qi to go through and nourish the limbs.

9. **Feet together:** Place feet flatly on the ground with the weight evenly distributed. If physically possible, the big toes and the heels of each foot should touch each other naturally.

   Purpose: With the inner feet touching each other, the Kidney Meridian and Yinxiao Meridian will be connected, enhancing the cultivation of Kidney Qi.

B. Mental preparation

After the body achieves the proper posture, relax the whole body from head to toe. The mind intent begins to expand and to permeate through the body. When mind intent reaches the head, imagine the head touching blue sky. When mind intent reaches the feet, imagine the feet touching the earth.

In order to achieve this kind of visualization, we must expand from the inside out. The intent is to expand from inside the body outward to infinity. The mind also permeates through the skin to achieve the feeling that the skin does not exist and that the body and the universe are one.

Respect ourselves and the Tao (surroundings and nature) to calm the mind. With a respectful and calm mind, the chaos of daily life will begin to recede into nothingness.

I. Opening

Rotate the hands backward and then downward, press the earth to collect qi. Then push forward 15 degrees and pull back to the beginning position. Repeat 3 times. Fig 1-2, 1-3, 1-4, 1-5.

Fig 1-2

Fig 1-3

Fig 1-4

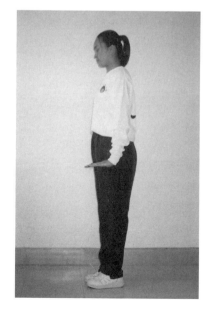

Fig 1-5

Relax wrists and turn palms to face each other. The hands lift qi upward to the navel level and deliver it to the Dantien through the navel. Fig 1-6, 1-7.

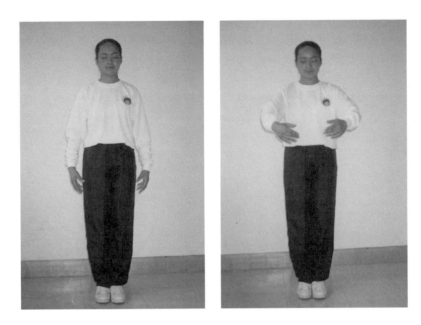

Fig 1-6   Fig 1-7

Turn palms down and circle them around to the side. Fig 1-8, 1-9.

Fig 1-8   Fig 1-9

Continue to turn and scoop qi to the back. Point to Mingmen and deliver qi to the Dantien through Mingmen. Fig 1-10, 1-11.

Fig 1-10   Fig 1-11

Move the hands upward and forward to the underarms; with the tips of the middle fingers slightly press Dabao and deliver qi inside. Rotate elbows backward until fingers point to the front. Fig 1-12, 1-13.

Fig 1-12   Fig 1-13

Extend the hands forward with palms up to shoulder level and width. Slightly bend the middle fingers to reflect qi into the head through Yintang (between the eyebrows). Rotate the arms 45 degrees until palms are facing each other diagonally; then circle the arms around to the sides forming a straight line. Fig 1-14, 1-15.

Fig 1-14   Fig 1-15

Rotate the arms to turn the hands down, then up to scoop qi upward. Lift hands upward in a circular motion until the hands are above the head. Put hands together and lift upward farther. Then lower the hands to the chest level forming a praying position. Fig 1-16, 1-17.

Fig 1-16   Fig 1-17

Details

1. Leading with the little fingers, rotate arms until palms are facing backward. With the knuckles of the middle fingers closest to the palms as pivot points, raise the fingers and press down the wrists until the palms face the ground. The hands and forearms form a 90-degree angle. With arms naturally extended, push the centers of the palms downward and forward to about one hand's length from the seams of the pants; arms and body forming an approximately 15-degree angle. Release the pressure, cup palms, and pull the arms back to the beginning position. Repeat this movement three times. Fig 1-2 to 1-5.

   The push and pull are not isolated movements but whole body movements. Using the shoulder joints as pivot points, the arms are being pushed and pulled by the Mingmen and Dantien. At the same time, the centers of the feet are pushing and pulling up and down. The arms and legs remain straight but never locked the entire time.

2. Relax wrists and rotate arms until the palms face each other, the fingers slightly bent as if holding a qi ball. Using the shoulder joints as pivot points, move arms up until the middle fingers are parallel to the navel. The distance between the hands should be shoulder width. Slightly bend tips of the middle fingers toward the navel to deliver qi into the Dantien. Fig 1-6 to 1-7.

   With wrists remaining at navel level, rotate arms until the palms face the ground. Then circle arms around and to the back as if the fingertips are touching the horizon and the palms are connected to the ground. When the hands reach the back and the wrists are about shoulder width, turn arms outward, bend elbows, rotate wrists, and slightly cup the palms. Turn palms by bending the little fingers until the palms face Mingmen and deliver qi into the Dantien. Fig 1-8 to 1-11.

   Extend elbows outward and rotate wrists until the palms are facing upward. Lift forearms until middle fingers touch Dabao (located on the side of the ribs under the arms, parallel to the nipples). Deliver qi inside the middle Dantien-- the chest. Fig 1-12 to 1-13.

3. Circle elbows toward the back until fingers are pointing to the front. At this point, distance between the elbows is about shoulder width, and the little fingers are touching the ribs. Then extend forearms forward and upward until wrists are at shoulder height and width. Cup palms, bend tips of the middle fingers slightly toward the head, and deliver qi into the upper Dantien through Yintang. Fig 1-14.

Rotate arms 45 degrees and circle arms around to the sides to form a straight line. The shoulders moves the elbows and the elbows move the hands. When the arms almost form a straight line, rotate arms to scoop hands down then up. Slowly circle arms up to above the head; then put the hands together. Use shoulders to push elbows, elbows to push hands, and hands to push fingers up as high as possible toward the sky. At the same time, pull up Baihui and pull down the tailbone. Fig 1-15 to 1-16.

Extend elbows to the sides to lower hands along the body center line. When wrists almost touch Baihui, move them forward to the forehead and continue downward, as if hands are inside the body, to front of the chest, forming a praying position. Fig 1-17.

Note: All the rotations are whole-arm movements pivoting at the shoulder joints, and leading with the little fingers.

Purpose

The main purpose is to collect the universal qi from earth and heaven and blend it with our own qi. Since most of the movements lead with the little finger which belongs to the Heart Meridian, qi is activated in the Heart Meridian to nourish the heart. When the fingers touch each other in the praying position, qi circulates between them, forming a loop to balance left and right sides of the body. Holding the hands in front of the chest in praying position is very spiritual and helps us to concentrate.

II. Crane's Neck and Dragon's Horns

A. Postures

1. Crane's Neck

Separate and lower hands along the rib cage. Then rest hands on the waist with thumbs slightly pressing Jinmen pressure points at the tip of 12th ribs. Tuck in the chin, and push and pull the cervical vertebrae backward and upward. Lean the head backward while pulling up the chin and Baihui. Fig 2-1, 2-2. 2-3.

Fig 2-1

Fig 2-2   Fig 2-3

Relax the cervical vertebrae and move the chin from upward to forward, downward, inward, and along the chest upward to complete the circular motion, returing to the beginning position. Fig 2-4, 2-5, 2-6, 2-7. Repeat 9 times.

Fig 2-4

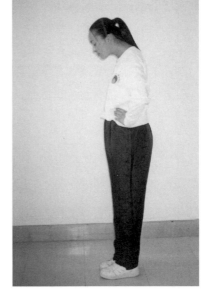

Fig 2-5

Fig 2-6

Fig 2-7

Opposite direction

Using the same principles, draw circle in the opposite direction . Repeat 9 times. Fig 2-7 to 2-1

2. Dragon's Horns

The "bulges" on the skull bone , which are approximately 2 inches above the ears, are called dragon's horns. The left dragon's horn moves downward diagonally to the left shoulder, then pushes up and to the right to draw a semicircle, returning to the beginning position (Fig 2-8, 2-9). Likewise, the right dragon's horn turns to the right to draw a semicircle (Fig 2-10, 2-11). Repeat the movements 18 times, 9 to each side.

Fig 2-8

Fig 2-9

Fig 2-10

Fig 2-11

B. Details

From the praying position, slowly separate wrists until tips of the middle finger touch the sternum. Move fingers along the edge of the rib cage, lower hands to the waist, then turn hands until the palms are facing upward. Leading with the little fingers, the hands continue to turn backward and downward to rest on the waist. The thumbs slightly pressing Jinmen (tip of 12th rib) and the rest of the fingers slightly pressing Zhangmen (slightly in front and under the tip of the 11th rib) and Daimai (about 1.8 inches underneath Zhangmen). Jinmen points are junction points for vertical meridian channels. If Jinmen were pressed, qi would flow into the vertical meridian channels instead of the membranes.

1. Crane's Neck

Forward direction crane's neck

The forward direction focuses on the cervical vertebrae pushing backward and pulling upward. By moving the head around Dazhui (Thoracic-1) as the pivot point through extending and bending the cervical vertebrae as the chin draws circles, we imitate the head movements of a walking crane. The purpose of this movement is to exercise the cervical vertebrae and the head.

a. **First tuck in the chin:** Baihui moves forward and downward as if looking at the shirt buttons. The chin tucks in to the limit. Fig 2-1.

b. **Pull the cervical vertebrae:** Hold the chin position as the cervical vertebrae push backward and upward. With Baihui leading, the head pushes upward and pulls up each cervical vertebra, one at a time. Fig 2-2.

c. **Lean the head backward:** With the chin still tucked in, lean the head backward to the limit. Relax Yuzheng and Baihui. Fig 2-3.

d. **Move the chin upward:** As the neck begins to relax Baihui pulls upward and backward. At the same time, the chin moves upward to the limit to start drawing a circle. Fig 2-4.

e. **Forward and downward:** The chin continues to move forward and downward to draw a circle. Fig 2-5

f. **Inward:** Baihui moves forward, downward and inward, as if to touch the chest, to help the chin move inward. This will create a downward and inward force in Baihui, and a backward and upward force in the chin. Imagine the chin brushing the thoracic vertebrae and pulling the cervical vertebrae upward, from number seven to Yuzhen, one vertebra at a time. Fig 2-6 to 2-7.

Using Dazhui as the pivotal point, and following steps **a** to **f**, we drew a complete circle. Repeat 9 times.

Backward (reverse) direction

This movement imitates the crane eating and drinking. The principles are the same for the reverse movements as for the forward movements except the steps are in opposite directions.

a. **Tuck in the chin:** Tuck in the chin until it touches the throat and hold the position.

b. **Move the chin downward:** Baihui pulls upward, forward and downward. Chin moves downward as if brushing the inner side of the cervical vertebrae.

c. **Forward and upward:** The chin pushes forward and then upward. Following the upward movement of the chin, the body pulls upward at the same time until the chin cannot move anymore.

d. **Pull cervical vertebrae:** Move Baihui backward and pull cervical vertebrae upward. At the same time tuck in the chin.

e. **Tuck in the chin:** Continue to push and pull up Baihui, tucking in the chin until it touches the throat.

The movements from **a,** to **e,** form a circle. Repeat 9 times.

Common mistakes: The movements of the chin tucking in and Baihui pulling upward are not synchronized. They should be done at the same time. In the movements of the head leaning backward and the chin moving upward and forward, the chin's path is not round enough.

Keys to the crane's neck practice

Tucking in the chin, pushing out and pulling up the cervical vertebrae. In the beginning stage of practice, use the chin to draw a maximum circle while Dazhui serves as a stationary point. In the more advanced stage, the chin should synchronize with the shoulder's open-close movements and the chest's convex-concave movements. For example, in the forward movements, when pulling up the cervical vertebrae, lean the body slightly backward, open the shoulder, and open up the chest so it expands in a convex fashion. As the chin moves forward and downward, the shoulders move slightly forward and inward as the chest moves in a concave fashion.

In the reverse direction, as the chin moves downward, the shoulders move forward and inward and the chest moves in a concave direction. In the upward motions, the shoulders open up, the chest opens and expands in a convex direction. The whole body relaxes.

With the movements of the body, shoulder, chest and chin, all of the vertebrae will behave like a string of pearls. Once the top one moves, the rest will follow it. A skilled practitioner will experience several frontal-backward curves in the spine.

2. Dragon's Horns

a. **Head leans to the left:** The left dragon's horn leans to the left, and the left shoulder and left ribs relax. The left ribs slightly move downward as the head leans to the left to the maximum, touching left ear to left shoulder. The left dragon's horn then pushes outward and upward, back to the beginning position. Fig 2-8 to 2-9.

b. **Head leans to the right:** The right dragon's horn leans to the right, and the right shoulder and right ribs relax. The right ribs slightly move downward as the head leans to the right to the maximum, touching right ear to right shoulder. The right dragon's horn pushes outward and upward, back to the beginning position. Fig 2-10 to 2-11.

Common mistakes: Using too much force and not relaxing enough when pushing upward with the horn. The head just sways from side to side. The chin moves too much.

Keys to the dragon's horns practice

Keep the chin stationary, the face always facing the front. Use the dragon's horns to draw a sleeping 8 or an infinity sign. When first learning the movements, use hands to help push up the dragon's horns. Put both hands on dragon's horns, and lean the head to the left. Relaxing the left side of the body (including the waist) will automatically lean the body to the left. Then the left hand pushes the left dragon's horn up; the horn is pulled up; and the body is pulled up at the same time. As the left horn reaches the top, lean to the right and push upward. If we relax the entire body, each vertebra in the spine will move.

At the beginning, we may draw a big sleeping figure 8. Once we become proficient, the movement should become smaller and less rigid. The smaller the head movement, the bigger the reaction from the spine. A skilled practitioner will experience side-to-side curves in the spine like a snake. The spinal motions occur only when the dragon's horns have an upward movement.

C. Purpose

By tucking in the chin and pulling up the cervical vertebrae, we open up pressure points, activate qi, and move qi up the Governing Meridian. When the head leans back, then moves upward, relaxing Yuzhen, qi will move from the tailbone, to Dazhui, to Yuzhen, and finally reach Baihui. As the head moves forward and downward with the chin tucked in, qi will be moved down to the Conception Meridian and Dantien. By doing the simple crane's neck movement, we activate the Governing and Conception Meridians.

With the hands pressing Jinmen, Zhangmen and Daimai and the synchronization of the body movements to open and close, pulling the cervical vertebrae can activate the body's Main Meridians. Although Chi-Lel™ Qigong does not focus on the Microcosmic Orbit, one crane's neck is roughly equivalent to one Microcosmic Orbit. Practicing crane's neck will reap the same benefits.

The dragon's horns movement activate the Gallbladder Meridian first and then stimulate the Liver Meridian. According to Traditional Chinese Medicine, Shuyang qi (qi in the Gallbladder Meridian) can activate the Chingyang qi in the inner organs. If we practice dragon's horns with the eyes closed, we will gradually feel the body getting light accompanied by a very comfortable upward feeling. This is the sensation of Chingyang qi moving upward. When Chingyang qi concentrates in the head, the brain will be nourished.

Activating the Governing, Conception and Gallbladder Meridians by exercising the head increases and strengthens the circulation of qi to the head to nourish the brain. The snake-like movements in the spine not only loosen up and stretch the vertebrae, but also massage the spinal cord and increase blood flow in the spine. Practicing this exercise can improve blood and lymphatic circulation in the neck and head areas. It is very effective in treating vertigo, headache, tinnitus and nervous system abnormalities.

III. Squeeze Shoulder Blades and Shrink Neck

A. Postures

Following the last movement, relax the hands, and rotate palms upward to face the sky. Move forearms forward to form a right angle (90 degrees) with the upper arms. Lift upper arms to shoulder level with the fingers pointing to the sky while maintaining the 90-degree angle between the forearms and upper arms. Fig 3-1, 3-2, 3-3.

Fig 3-1

Fig 3-2

Fig 3-3

Circle upper arms to the sides. Rotate palms outward, lower forearms to form a straight line. Then move the forearms up and down 3 times. Fig 3-4, 3-5, 3-6, 3-5a, 3-6a.

Fig 3-4   Fig 3-5

Fig 3-6   Fig 3-5a   Fig 3-6a

With the arms forming a straight line and the palms facing downward, rotate wrists forward and backward 3 times each using middle fingers to draw circles. Fig 3-7, 3-8

Fig 3-7   Fig 3-8

With the head slightly leaning backward, tuck in the chin and shrink the neck while the shoulder blades are squeezed in and the tailbone is raised upward. Extend the shoulders and relax the neck and tailbone. Then return to the original position. Fig 3-9, 3-10, 3-11, 3-12. Repeat 3 times.

Fig 3-9   Fig 3-10

Fig 3-11   Fig 3-12

The left shoulder blade propels the right shoulder blade upward and pushes the right arm outward as the left arm contracts. The right shoulder then does the same thing to the left shoulder. Repeat 9 times and return to the beginning position. Fig 3-13, 3-14, 3-15, 3-16.

Fig 3-13   Fig 3-14

Fig 3-15   Fig 3-16

B. Details

1. Open arms and rotate wrists

Following the last movement, relax and release the hands from the waist. Rotate hands until palms face the sky as elbows move to the back to form a straight line with the forearms and fingers move to the front. Move the forearms forward until elbows touch the ribs. Foreams form a 90 degree angle with the upper arms. Using shoulder joints as pivots, move elbows upward to shoulder level with palms facing the back and the fingers pointing to the sky. Maintain 90-degree angle between forearm and upper arm. Fig 3-1 to 3-3.

Circle arms to both sides. After upper arms form a straight line, turn palms outward leading with the little fingers. Then lower forearms to form a straight line. Using elbows as pivot points, move forearms up to form 90 degrees with the upper arms, leading with the middle fingers. Palms face outward; forearms and fingers point to the sky. Lower forearms to form a straight linc. Repeat this sequence 3 times. Fig 3-4 to 3-6a.

With arms forming a straight line, fingers naturally extended, and the palms facing the ground, rotate wrists. Using wrists as pivot points, shoulders and elbows stationary, draw 3 circles with the hands-- first to the front, down, back and up. Lead with the middle fingers. Palms face the ground at all times. Next draw 3 circles in the opposite direction. Return hands and arms to one straight line. The rotations should be round and agile, slow and even. Fig 3-7 to 3-8.

Common mistakes: Upper arms are not parallel to the ground. Arms are not opened completely to form a straight line. Palms are turned to the front instead of to the side. Elbow and hand do not form a straight line.

Keys to the practice

While circling arms to the side, expand the shoulders and the chest and maintain the right angle between the forearms and upper arms. Maintain the upright forearm position throughout the movement. While rotating the palms outward, do not bend the wrists; the hands and forearms maintain straight lines. Fingers should not bend, palms face the ground and forearms remain stationary when drawing circles with the wrists.

Pay attention to the continuity of the movements. The movements may look rectangular outside, but the inner feeling should be circular. Once the techniques are mastered, do not wait until one movement stops before starting a new one. The transition from one movement to another should be seamless. For example, we should begin to circle arms to the side as the elbows reach approximately 3/4 the distance upward to the shoulder level. The path becomes an arch instead of a rectangle.

2. Squeeze shoulder blades and shrink neck

a. **Squeezing the shoulder blades:** Using the fingertips, slightly pull the arms outward to form a straight line. Contract shoulder blades toward the 4th thoracic vertebra, and slightly bend and sink the elbows. The wrists are at shoulder height with the fingers naturally extended and pointing slightly upward. Fig 3-9.

b. **Shrink neck:** The body does not move. Lean the head back, tuck in the chin and shrink the neck downward. Point tailbone slightly backward and upward toward the fourth thoracic vertebra. Fig 3-10 to 3-11.

Common mistakes: Squeeze the elbows instead of shoulder blades. Wrists drop below the shoulder. Chin is not tucked in. Mingmen is pressed in.

Keys to the practice

The body does not move. The four points – the head (leans backward), the chin (tucks in), the shoulder blades (squeeze inward), and the tailbone (points backward and upward) – all contract toward the 4th thoracic vertebra at the same time. In releasing, the four points expand outward simultaneously.

3. Waving Arms Movement

In the waving arms movements, the left side is contracted while the right side is being extended and vice versa. The movements are snake-like. When the right shoulder blade moves toward the spine, the left shoulder blade moves outward to the left. Simultaneously, the right upper arm squeezes inward through the shoulder joint, the right elbow sinks slightly, and the right wrist bends. The fingers move naturally. Similar movements are repeated on the left side. Alternating movements of the shoulders result in an infinity sign when shoulders are viewed from the back. Fig 3-13 to 3-15.

Common mistakes: Both hands fall below the straight horizontal line. Shoulder blades are not contracting and extending. Body is not centered and is leaning to the left and then right.

Keys to the practice
Both arms move at the same time, but focus is placed on the primary side. The arms maintain a straight, horizontal line. With the contracting and extending, the arms have an up and down movement. The contracting side is slightly below the horizontal line and the extending side is slightly above the horizontal line. The contraction and extension should be performed simultaneously.

C. Purpose

These movements are designed to expand the chest, open up the shoulder joints, and relax the elbows and fingers. Expanding and circling arm movements increases lung capacity and improves circulation in the heart.

Normally, the area between the shoulder blades is seldom exercised. Squeezing the shoulders and contracting the neck will exercise and massage this area. There are many important pressure points in this area which regulate qi flow to the heart and lungs. Squeezing the shoulders will activate and strengthen these points. Consequently, heart and lungs are strengthened. Snake-like movements are designed to loosen up and maintain the agility of the upper body. Overall, this section is very effective in treating and preventing arthritis in the upper limbs as well as problems in the shoulder blades.

IV. Erect Palms, Separate Fingers, and Open Meridians

A. Postures

Fig 4-1

The arms form a straight line at shoulder level. The body is centered. Leading with the middle fingers, erect the palms to form right angles with the forearms by thrusting the center of the palms outward and pulling the fingers backward. With the arms maintaining a straight line, contract the shoulder blades inward toward each other and then push out with the upper arms and wrists. Fig 4-1. Repeat 3 to 5 times.

With the palms and forearms still forming right angles, separate the fingers. First separate the thumbs and the little fingers, and then the index and ring fingers. Push the palms outward. Fig 4-2, 4-3

Fig 4-2

Fig 4-3

Close the fingers - index and ring fingers first, followed by the thumbs and little fingers. Repeat Open and Close 5 to 7 times. Fig 4-4, 4-5.

Fig 4-4   Fig 4-5

Relax the hands, curl the fingers downward like a claw, one joint at a time until the fingertips touch. Move the fingertips toward the center of the palms. Fig.4-6, 4-6a, 4-7. 4-7a.

Fig 4-6   Fig 4-7

Erect the wrists, and straighten the fingers one joint at a time. Fig. 4-8, 4-8a, 4-9, 4-9a. Repeat claw hand movements 3 to 5 times.

Fig 4-8   Fig 4-9

Fig 4-6a   Fig 4-7a   Fig 4-8a   Fig 4-9a

Leading with the middle fingers, lower the hands to form a straight line with the arms. Repeat waving arms movements 3 times. Fig 3-12 to 3-16.

70

B. Details

1. **Erect the palms:** The body is centered. The arms are level and form a straight line. Leading with the middle fingers, erect the palms to form a right angle with the forearms. Leading with the wrists, the arms push outward, loosen up the shoulder and elbow joints. At the same time, the center of the palms, wrists, and fingers thrust outward, and the back of the hands and the fingertips pull backward.

   After the correct posture is obtained, the shoulder blades contract toward each other with the arms maintaining a straight line. The fingers are straight, and the palms are erect. While pushing the arms outward, push the wrists and center of the palms forward and pull back the fingertips to the maximum. Repeat 3 to 5 times. Fig 4-1.

   Common mistakes: Centers of palms are not pushed outward in thrust outward motion. Elbows are bent in contracting motion.

2. **Separate the fingers:** Following the last movement, push the palms outward and separate the fingers. First separate the thumbs and the little fingers simultaneously; then separate the index and ring fingers. The motion should be slow and even. Separate to the limit, and push the palms outward. Close the index and ring fingers, followed by the thumbs and the little fingers. Repeat 5 to 7 times. Fig 4-2 to 4-5.

   Common mistakes: Fingers are not erect. Wrists are not pushed out.

3. **Curl the fingers:** After separating the fingers, curl them downward. First relax the wrists; then the fingers and the palms curl downward. Beginning with the fingertips, use force to intentionally curl the fingers downward, one joint at a time, forming an eagle claw. Continue to move the fingers downward until the fingertips touch. At this time, the palms and the forearms should form a 45-degree angle; pull the fingertips toward the centers of the palms forming an empty fist. Erect the palms; then relax and extend the fingers one joint at a time from the palm to the finger tips. Repeat 3 to 5 times. Fig 4-6 to 4-9a.

   Common mistakes: Fingers are not curled downward one joint at a time. Thumb and little finger are not touching each other while pulling toward the center of palm. Wrist is bent more than 45 degrees.

4. **Waving arm movements:** Same as in **III. Shoulders and Neck.**

Keys to the practice

The arms need to be straight and level at all times. The method to determine whether arms are level or not is not by using eyes but by relaxing both arms. If the hands are heavy and the shoulders are light, then the hands are too low. If the hands are light and the shoulders are heavy, the hands are too high. While pushing outward, the wrists remain stationary and the fingertips are pulled back toward the head. Thus, qi will return to the body. In contracting the shoulder blades inward, the force remains horizontal. During the movements, the head, the body and the tailbone do not move.

In curling the fingers, the hands act like eagle claws ready to catch a fish; the attention is on the fingertips. Relax the wrists first, then curl downward. The main movements are centered on first and second joints of the fingers. When the fingertips close into the center of the palms, they are still touching each other; the wrists should not curl inward. This movement is designed to tense the outer arm tendons and to relax those of the inner arms. In uncurling the fingers, the outer sides of the arms will relax and the inner sides will tense.

C. Purpose

The main purpose for these movements is to activate the six meridians in the hands. The three Hand Yin Meridians originate in the chest and run through the inner arms to the fingers; the three Hand Yang Meridians originate in the fingers and run through the outer arms to the head. By tensing and relaxing the inner and outer arms through the finger movements, we activate both Yin and Yang Meridians. Separate finger movements stretch the inner arms and mainly exercise the three Hand Yin Meridians; curling finger movements stretch the outer arms and exercise the three Hand Yang Meridians. Yin and Yang qi will nourish each other.

Besides activating the meridians, this exercise focuses on strengthening the Jing pressure points. With the exception of the Jong Chong pressure points, which are located in the fingertips, the rest of the fingers' Jing pressure points are located at the base of the fingernails. Jing pressure points allow qi to circulate in and out of the meridians. By exercising the fingers, qi and blood will rush to the fingertips, dissolving any blockage in the finger meridians. The qi in the fingertips will be plentiful and circulate strongly and uninterrupted. The functions of Jing pressure points will be strengthened. As a result, the qi in all six Hand Meridians will circulate smoother and stronger. The other benefits are listed in section IV. Since the Yang Meridians are the small and large intestine meridians, this exercise is very good for the gastrointestinal system.

V. Yi Qi Thrust

A. Posture

Lower the arms and raise the hands to the chest to form a praying position. Lace the fingers while raising the hands upward to the front of the forehead. Slowly rotate the palms upward and push the arms forward to form an ellipse. Fig 5-1, 5-2.

Fig 5-1

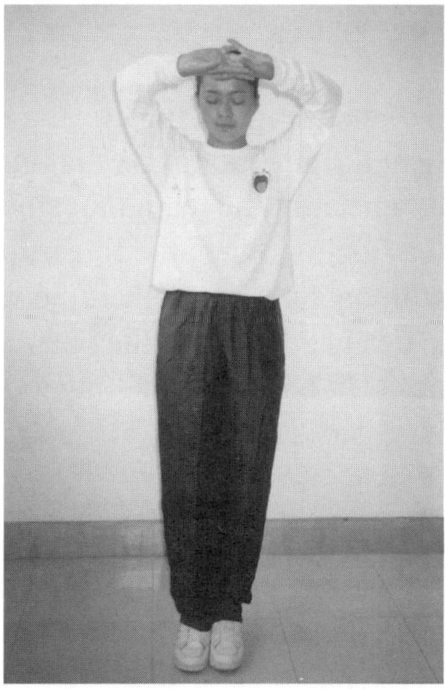

Fig 5-2

Turn the upper body to the left, with the face facing left, and form a 90-degree angle with the feet. The hands are in front of the forehead and the arms form an ellipse with the left upper arm at shoulder level and the right forearm at the same level as the right ear. Fig 5-3.

Fig 5-3

73

Thrust the right rib upward from the Dantien, then turn the upper body to the right by using the right ribs to pull the right shoulder, the right elbow and the hands to the front, forming an ellipse. The body is then facing forward with the thumbs at eye level, the right forearm at ear level and the left upper arm at shoulder level. Fig 5-4, 5-5.

Fig 5-4   Fig 5-5

Turn the upper body to the right, with the face facing right, and form a 90-degree angle with the feet. The hands are in front of the forehead and the arms form an ellipse with the right upper arm at shoulder level, and the left forearm is at the same level as the left ear. The hands are approximately one fist's length from the forehead. Fig 5-6.

Fig 5-6

Thrust the left ribs upward, and turn the upper body to the left by using the left ribs to pull the left shoulder, elbow and hands to the front to form an ellipse. The body is then facing forward, with the thumbs at eye level, the left forearm at ear level and the right upper arm at shoulder level. Fig 5-7, 5-8. Repeat 18 times.

Fig 5-7   Fig 5-8

After the last repetition, return hands to the beginning position. Fig 5-9

Fig 5-9

B. Details

This section consists of three parts: the body turning to the left and to the right, the arms forming a continually changing ellipse, and the qi thrusting.

1. **Beginning movements.** At the end of waving arm movements, slowly and evenly lower the arms to the sides and continually raise the hands upward to the chest level to form a praying position. Lace the fingers while moving the hands upward to the front of the forehead; then slowly rotate the palms upward and push the arms outward to form a slanting ellipse. Both arms (shoulder, elbows, wrists, palms and fingers) must rotate from inward to outward and upward, exerting an outward and upward isotonic force. At this point, the backs of the hands should be facing the forehead. Fig 5-1 to 5-2.

   Common Mistakes: Arms are too straight. Elbows are locked.

2. **Turning body and forming ellipse movements.**

   a. Turning the body: Relax the body and turn the waist to the left until the upper body is facing left and forming a 90-degree angle with the front. In the beginning, minimize hip movement when turning the waist. In more advance practice, the lower limbs move naturally with the waist movements during the turn. Then do the same movements turning to the right.

   b. The movements of the arm while turning: During the left turn, the left arm pulls the right arm to the left side (left shoulder pulls left elbow, left elbow pulls left hand, left hand pulls right hand, right hand pulls right elbow, right elbow pulls right shoulder). The same is true for the right turn. Fig 5-3.

   c. The positions of the arms: From the front to the left side, lower the left upper arm along the left ear to the shoulder level, with the right forearm at the right ear level. From the left back to the front, the arms form a "right up - left down" ellipse. From the front to the right, lower the right upper arm along the right ear to the shoulder level, with the left forearm at the left ear level. From the right back to the front, the arms form a "left up - right down" ellipse. During the whole movement, both arms maintain the outward and upward isotonic force. Fig 5-4 to 5-9.

   d. The relationship between the hands and the forehead: The hands are always in front of the forehead. When facing the sides, the hands are approximately one fist's length (10 cm) from the forehead; when facing the front, they are about an arm's length from the forehead.

The combination of **a**, **b**, **c** and **d** constitutes the "turning the body and forming the ellipse" movements.

Common mistakes: Hands move by themselves. The waist is not turning. The following hand pushes the leading hand. Leaning the body sideways during the turn.

Keys: The body is always centered. The middle fingers are always in front of the eyes. The shape of the ellipse changes with the body movement.

3. Qi thrusting

Thrusting area. Place the hands on the ribs with the tips of the thumbs slightly below the nipples. The areas located under the centers of the palms are the targets for the qi to thrust to.

Qi thrust. Use Dantien qi to thrust as if pushing someone to the side. Turn the body to the left side; thrust the right ribs (Qi thrusts from the Dantien to the right target area. The right ribs push the right shoulder. The right shoulder pushes out the right arm). Turn the body to the right side; thrust the left ribs (Qi thrusts from Dantien to the left target area. The left ribs push the left shoulder. The left shoulder pushes out the left arm).

Common mistakes: Shoulder thrust instead of qi thrust from the Dantien.

Keys: Do not use the lower arm to push the upper arm after the thrust. The thrusting is a slanting upward motion. Keep upper body centered before, and after the thrust; do not lean to one side.

C. Purpose

The rib area is one of the weakest parts of the body, yet Shuyang Meridians run through the ribs. Conditions in this area have a direct influence on the Bladder Meridians. While thrusting the ribs, Shuyang Bladder Meridians will be activated and strengthened. This exercise is good for the liver, the bladder, the diaphragm and the pleura (lining of the lung).

VI. Bend Body, Arch Spine, and Loosen Governing Meridians

A. Posture

Move hands upward to the top of the head with fingers still joined together. Straighten arms when the palms face the sky. Relax the shoulders and arms. Push hands upward as if pushing an object. The wrists alternately draw a front-up—and-back-down circle. Repeat 3 to 5 times. Fig 6-1, 6-2, 6-3.

Fig 6-1

Fig 6-2

Fig 6-3

Separate hands with palms facing forward and the upper arms touching the ears. Both the head and the arms move and extend forward, relax the waist and the back. The thoracic and lumbar vertebrae arch forward. The head and the hands move forward and downward as the waist bends forward, and the vertebrae curl downward from cervical to thoracic to lumbar until the hands touch the floor, the back forming an arch. With palms touching the ground, press the hands downward three times Fig 6-4, 6-5, 6-6, 6-7.

Fig 6-4

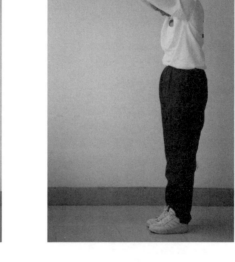

Fig 6-5

Fig 6-6

Fig 6-7

Turn to the left and press three times. Turn to the right and press three times. Fig 6-8, 6-9

Fig 6-8   Fig 6-9

Return back to the center. Scoop qi backward with the hands until the thumbs and the middle and index fingers are touching the Achilles tendon. Massage the tendon three times. Retract the stomach and push out the waist three times with the head touching the knees. Fig 6-10, 6-11.

Fig 6-10   Fig 6-11

The hands scoop qi back to the front. With the upper arms touching the ears, move the back upward, one vertebra at a time from lumbar to thoracic to cervical and return to the beginning position. Relax the body naturally. Fig 6-12, 6-13. Repeat the movements (Fig 6-5 to 6-13) 5 to 7 times.

Fig 6-12

Fig 6-13

After the last repetition, turn palms to face each other, lower the hands along the rib cage and rest them on the waist. Fig 6-14

Fig 6-14

B. Details

1. **Rotate the wrists:** Move the hands to above the head with the fingers interlaced and the palms facing upward. Straighten and pull the arms upward, relaxing the shoulders and arms. Rotate one hand slightly as if the hand were pushing an object upward; then repeat with the other hand. The wrists alternately draw a front-up-back-down circle. Begin, for example, moving the left wrist forward and upward, followed by pushing the left shoulder upward and also pressing the left wrist upward. Straighten the left arm. The right arm with the elbow slightly bent is completely relaxed. Do the same movements with the right wrist. Stretch and move the wrists to draw vertical circles alternately. Fig 6-1 to 6-3.

    Common mistakes: Body leans to left and right. Chest is not relaxed. Tailbone is not pointing to the ground.

    Keys to the practice: During the movements, press wrists upward to the maximum and use the shoulders to push up to pull up every vertebrae and the rib cage. When this practice progresses, we should be able to pull up the heels and toes. At the beginning, we should at least be able to pull up the waist. The upper body movements should be as follows: the shoulder pushes the upper arm, the upper arm pushes the elbow, the wrist draws a vertical circle and pulls up the forearm. The vertebrae move upward continually from cervical to thoracic to lumbar. The chest should be hollow and relaxed. The stomach is tucked in. The waist is relaxed and pushing backward. Baihui pushes upward, and the chin is tucked in.

2. **Bend-body and arch-back movements.** Relax and separate the intertwined fingers and turn the palms forward. The shoulders push the elbows upward. The head remains centered; do not lean backward. With the vertebrae pulled up to the maximum, qi is pulled upward, and we might feel that the whole body is lifted. Next, relax the entire body beginning with the upper limbs, neck, chest, waist and then the lower limbs. Then, we might feel as if water is being poured down from the head to the toes. The pulled-up qi will permeate the whole body. Fig 6-4 to 6-7.

    Spine curls downward: With the upper arms touching the ears and the chin pulling inward touching the chest, push the back upward, pull hands forward and then downward. Tuck the head inward, and curl the seven cervical vertebrae downward one at a time. Hollow the chest, push the back upward and backward, and curl the twelve thoracic vertebrae downward one at a time. Withdraw the stomach, push the lower back backward, and curl the five lumbar vertebrae downward one at a time. When the spine cannot go down anymore, the hands can use a grasping motion to help the downward curling motion. Finally, sucking in the stomach will help push

82

the spine backward allowing the spine to go down further.

Common mistakes: Upper arms are not touching the ears. Cervical and thoracic vertebrae are not curling downward. Tailbone is not tucked in.

Purpose: This movement will loosen up each vertebra and the tendons in the spine adjusting the nervous system.

3. **Head - touches - legs movements**

    Press downward with the hands in front of the body: With palms touching the ground, fingers pointing to the front, wrists next to the toes, the arms relax, pressing downward. When pressing, the forehead touches the knees and pulls upward. Tuck in the abdomen and push the waist backward and upward. Press three times. Fig 6-7.

    Press downward with the hands pointing to the left: Turn to the left, with the palms touching the ground, fingers pointing to the left, and wrist next to the left outer foot. Relax arms and press downward. When pressing, the forehead touches the knees and pulls upward. Tuck in the abdomen and push the waist backward and upward. Press three times. Fig 6-8.

    Press downward with hands pointing to the right: Turn to the right, with the palms touching the ground, fingers pointing to the right, and wrist next to the right outer foot. Relax arms and press downward. When pressing, the forehead touches the knees and pulls upward. Tuck in the abdomen and push the waist backward and upward. Press three times. Fig 6-9.

    Press downward with the fingers touching the Achilles tendon: Return the body to the front. Hands scoop qi toward the ankles (the movement should be small; do not separate the hands too much). When the hands reach the ankles, the thumbs, index fingers and middle fingers touch and massage the Achilles tendons. At the same time, the forehead touches the knees and pulls upward. Tuck in the abdomen and push the waist backward and upward. Press three times. If unable to touch the Achilles tendons, pat the calves slightly. The center of gravity should be in the balls of the feet. Fig 6-10 to 6-11.

    Common mistakes: Knees are bent. Waist does not push backward.

    Purpose: The Bladder Meridian is located in the back of the legs. Massaging the Achilles tendons will adjust this meridian.

4. **Arching - upward movements:** The hands scoop qi toward the front until the upper arms touch the ears. With the tailbone tucked in and the hands held as if holding heavy objects, curl the spine upward one vertebra at a

time beginning with the lumbar vertebrae, followed by thoracic and cervical vertebrae. When the fingers are pointing to the sky, the upper arms still touching the ears, relax the body. Then use the arms to lead the whole body to do up-and-down, front-and-back relaxation movements. Fig 6-12 to 6-13.

Common mistakes: Upper arms are not touching the ears. Thoracic and cervical vertebrae are not curling upward one vertebra at a time. Use the waist to move up the whole body.

Keys to the practice: Although the purpose of this exercise is not to stretch the hamstrings, the legs should remain straight at all times. When bending down or coming up, the spine should curl up or down one vertebra at a time. The important part is to move the spine and loosen up the vertebrae.

C. Purpose

The main purpose of this section is to work on the Governing Meridian and Taiyang Bladder Meridian. The Governing Meridian governs the body Yang qi and the Foot Taiyang Bladder Meridians primarily transport qi to the inner organs. This is one of the most important methods for inducing qi into the bones. Arching and bending the spine loosen vertebrae and strengthen muscles and ligaments in the back. It is very effective in treating spine and back problems and in strengthening the nerve system.

VII. Turn Waist, Move Kua

A. Posture

Step on qi and separate feet to at least shoulder width and parallel to each other. Relax the hip joints and use them as pivot points to rotate the pelvic bone. Turn to the left (front, left, back and right) nine times, then to the right nine times Fig 7-1, 7-2, 7-3, 7-4, 7-5, 7-6.

Fig 7-1

Fig 7-2

Fig 7-3

Fig 7-4

Fig 7-5   Fig 7-6

Scoop the coccyx to the front and to the back in order to move the pelvic bone forward and back nine times. Fig. 7-7, 7-8.

Fig 7-7   Fig 7-8

B. Details

1. Hands-rest-on-waist, step-on-qi movements

Turn palms to face each other; then move hands downward along the rib cage to rest on the waist. Step on qi to separate feet to slightly wider than shoulder width. Lower the body slightly to create an angle between the body and the upper thighs; the knees cannot pass beyond the toes. Rotate the pelvic rim backward and downward while lowering the body to stabilize and root the lower body to the ground. At the same time, Baihui is pulled upward. By sitting downward and pulling upward, the waist area will be emptied. With the coccyx pointing to the ground and Huiyin raised, Dantien qi can be used to push Mingmen out to loosen up the waist. Fig 7-1 to 7-2.

2. Turn-waist and move-Kua movements

Overall requirements: The areas from the chest up and the knees down should remain immobile. Using the hip joints as supporting points and with mind intent on the coccyx, use the coccyx to move the pelvis to draw circles.

Circular movement requirement: Imagine standing on a map with the front of the body facing north. The coccyx moves from the center to the front (N), to the left front (NW), to the left (W), to the left back (SW), to the back (S), to the right back (SE), to the right (E), to the right front (NE), and then back to the front. Repeat three times and then reverse the direction. Fig 7-3 to 7-5.

To the front: Scoop the coccyx to the front, pull up Huiyin, and pull in the abdomen.
To the left front: Move the coccyx and the abdomen to the northwest.
To the left: The center of gravity for the pelvis shifts to the left hip joint. The left hip joint is higher than right hip joint; the left side is solid and the right side is empty. The buttocks point to the left.
The left back: Move the coccyx to the southwest.
The back: Move the coccyx backward to the maximum, press the waist, and relax Huiyin.
The right back: Move the coccyx to the southeast.
The right: The center of gravity for the pelvis shifts to the right hip joint. the right hip joint is higher than the left hip joint; the right side is solid and the left side is empty. The buttocks point to the right.
The right front: Move the coccyx and the abdomen to the northeast.

Common mistakes: The whole body moves. The coccyx is not drawing a circle.

3. **Scoop-the-coccyx front and back movement**
When scooping forward, contract the buttocks, Huiyin, pelvic floor muscles, and abdomen. Relax Huiyin and the pelvic floor muscles while scooping backward. Fig 7-7 to 7-8.

Common mistakes: The body bobs up and down.

Keys to the practice: At the beginning, the coccyx can draw a bigger circle, the feet can separate farther apart, and the body can lower a little bit farther. With practice, we use the Dantien and coccyx to draw small circles which are more effective. We use the body to lead the qi to turn in the beginning, the qi to turn the body in advance practice.

C. Purpose

This exercise loosens up the waist, turns the coccyx and closes Huiyin. It increases the storage of qi in the Dantien. Turning the coccyx activates the Yang qi to move up the Governing Meridian. It is very effective in treating bladder and reproductive problems. According to Traditional Chinese Medicine, kidney qi is prenatal qi and lung qi is postnatal qi. When kidney qi is not strong enough, prenatal qi cannot connect to postnatal qi. Movements in this section strength the kidney qi, connecting it with the lung qi to nourish the lungs.

88

VIII. Open Front and Back Kua

A. Postures

1. Open Front Kua

Fig 8-1

Following the last movement, the feet form a straight line by turning toes outward with the heels facing each other. The distance between the heels is approximately shoulder width. Straighten legs and center the body. Separate hands from the waist and turn palms to face the sky. Move forearms forward until the elbows touch the ribs and form a 90-degree angle with the upper arms. Lift the upper arms until palms face Yintang. Fig 8-1, 8-2, 8-3.

Fig 8-2

Fig 8-3

Turn the palms out with forearms and fingers pointing to the sky. Circle upper arms to the sides to form a straight line. Lower forearms to form a straight line. Fig 8-4, 8-5, 8-6.

Wave arms by contracting the left shoulder blade and extending the right shoulder blade, and vice versa. Repeat three times. Fig 3-11 to 3-14. Legs remain separated.

Fig 8-4   Fig 8-5

Fig 8-6

Bend the knees and lower the body till the thighs are parallel to the ground (the body remains straight), and simultaneously lower the arms. When the hands are lowered to knee level, bend the forearms forward and clasp the palms in front of the body. Erect and move the palms to the chest level and form a praying hands position. Fig 8-7, 8-8, 8-9.

Fig 8-7

Fig 8-8

Fig 8-9

Fig 8-10

Use the fingertips and wrist to draw three opposite-direction circles each way. Using the base knuckle of the third finger as a pivot point, the fingers circle in one direction while the wrists circle in the opposite direction. Fig 8-10, 8-10a, 8-11, 8-11a, 8-12, 8-12a, 8-13, 8-13a.

Fig 8-11   Fig 8-12

Fig 8-10a   Fig 8-11a

Fig 8-13   Fig 8-12a   Fig 8-13a

92

Leading with Baihui, straighten the body. Raise the hands upward along the chest to in front of Yintang and turn the palms outward. Fig 8-14, 8-15. Repeat movements Fig 8-4 to Fig 8-15 5 to 7 times. At the end of the last repetition, the hands are rested in front of the chest in the praying hands position with legs straightened.

Fig 8-14   Fig 8-15

2. Open back Kua

Following the last movement, turn left toes inward and right heel outward to form a straight line. The distance between the toes is approximately one foot's length. Lean the upper body forward about 35 degrees, straighten legs, point the buttocks to the back, and press the waist forward. Embrace the arms forward, relax the chest, and tuck in the chin. The middle fingers are pointing to each other and the palms are cupped at Yintang level. Fig 8-16, 8-17.

Fig 8-16   Fig 8-17

Bend the knees inward and sit down slightly. Move arms upward and
outward in a circular motion to the shoulder level as if holding a huge
balloon. Tuck in the abdomen and relax the waist. Relax the upper body
and lean backward (from the fourth thoracic vertebra upward) as if observing the sky. Fig 8-18. Push the head upward, straighten the legs, embrace
the arms forward and move back to Fig 8-16 position. Repeat movement
(Fig 8-16, 8-18) 5 to 7 times.

Fig 8-18

94

At the end of the last repetition, push the head upward, straighten the body, move the hands upward to above the head and to shoulder width in a circular motion. When hands face each other, cup the palms slightly; then lower the hands in front of the body and along the rib cage to rest on the waist. Step on qi to close the feet. Fig 8-19, 8-20.

Fig 8-19   Fig 8-20

B. Details

1. Open front Kua

a. **Turn the feet outward to form a straight line.** Following the last movement, use the heels as pivot points, turn the toes outward to form a straight line with the heels pointing at each other. The distance between the heels is approximately shoulder width. The legs are straight and the body is centered. Fig 8-1.

   Note: When turning the toes, the feet must be touching the floor at all times. Do not use the eyes to watch the turning. Do not turn the body with the toes. Beginners can turn one foot at a time, and put mind intent on the big and little toes to stabilize the body.

   Common mistake: Heels are too close to each other. Body leaning forward.

b. Arm movements. Separate the hands from the waist, turn palms upward, and point fingers to the front. Move elbows backward and inward and move forearms forward. The elbows point downward and touch the ribs to form a right angle with the upper arms. Use the shoulder joints as pivot points and the elbows as moving points. Move the upper arms upward until the hands are in front of the forehead with the fingers pointing to the sky and the palms facing Yintang. At the same time, move the elbows inward to a distance that is slightly narrower than shoulder width. Fig 8-2 to 8-5.

Leading with the little fingers, turn the palms outward and rest the thumbs in front of Yintang. Use the shoulder joints as pivot points to circle the upper arms to the sides forming a straight line. While circling, the hands and the elbows move at the same time. Keep the thumbs at Yintang level and imagine that they are inside Yintang and pulling it open. Fig 8-4 to 8-5.

After the upper arms form a straight line, lower the forearms. The arm movements should be continuous. The waving arm movements in the shoulder cause the upper body, the waist, the hips and then the lower limbs to naturally sway to and fro. Fig 8-6.

Common mistakes: Arms do not form a straight line. Chest does not expand to the sides.

c. Lower the body and the hands to form a praying position. When lowering the body, bend the knees, sit on the pelvis, and point the knees in the same direction as the toes. At the same time, lower hands to the knee level. By the time hands almost touch the knees, thighs should be parallel to the ground. Move the forearms forward to scoop qi; then put the hands together and move them to the chest to form a praying hands position. Fig 8-7 to 8-9.

Common mistakes: Lower hands and body movements are not coordinated.

d. Turn the hands in front of the chest. The forearms form a straight line and the wrists are fixed. Using the third joint of the middle finger as the fixed point, draw circles with the fingertips and the wrist. The forearms maintain a straight line, and the hands form right angles with the forearms. The shoulders, the elbows and the waist will follow the movements of the fingertips and the wrist. Fig 8-10 to 8-13.

Common mistakes: While sitting down, the body leans forward; knees are not pointing to the same direction of toes.

e. **Turn the palms.** In the left turn, the fingertips point to the front and the wrists to the back; the left hand pushes the right hand. When the fingertips point to the left front, the wrists point to the right back; the fingertips point to the left, the wrists point to the right; the fingertips point to the left back, the wrists point to the right front; the fingertips point to the back, the wrists point to the front. Then the right hand pushes the left hand. The fingertips point to the right back, the wrists point to the left front; the fingertips point to the right, the wrists point to the left; the fingertips point to the right front, the wrists point to the left back. Repeat 3 times and then reverse the direction. Fig 8-10a to 8-13a.

Common mistakes: Fingers are not pointing to the sky all the time. Wrists are not drawing circles.

f. **Straighten the body.** Leading with Baihui, straighten the body by squeezing the hands as if the fingertips are touching the skull and push the body upward. At the same time, move arms up. Relax the elbows and turn them slightly inward to a distance slightly shorter than shoulder width. When the body is straight, the palms should be in front of Yintang. Repeat **a.** to **e.** 5 to 7 times. At the last repetition, maintain the praying hands position while straightening the body. Fig 8-14.

Common mistakes: Use the legs to push the body upward.

2. Open back Kua (Sacroiliac joint)

Following the last movement, turn the left toes inward and the right heel outward to form a straight line. The distance between the toes is approximately one foot's length; it can be adjusted by shifting the right foot's center of gravity. Use the big toes to stabilize the body.

a. **Embrace forward.** Straighten legs and stretch legs toward the back; the pelvis moves backward. Move the tailbone outward, backward, and scoop upward; press the waist forward. The upper body leans forward at 35 degrees. Hold the arms forward at shoulder level as if embracing a tree. The hands are approximately three inches apart, with the middle fingers and thumbs at Yintang level. The palms face the body as if holding a ball; the chest is hollow and relaxed. Tuck the chin in and raise Baihui. The mind focuses on the center of the thumbs. Fig 8-16 to 8-18.

Note: It is normal to see white light after holding the position a long period of time. When that happens, ignore it.

Common mistakes: Body leans forward too much. Chest protrudes outward instead of opening. Pressing the Mingmen inward instead of the waist. Legs are not straightened. The big toes do not press down. Tailbone does not scoop backward and upward.

b.   **Observe the sky.** Relax knees. Then bend and turn the knees slightly inward, rotating thighs inward. Move the hands up and out in a circular motion to ear level, forming an arch with the arms and the palms facing the sky as if holding an giant ball. Relax the waist, hips and coccyx. Pull the abdomen in and lean backward from the fourth thoracic vertebra. Tuck the chin in and raise Baihui. With eyes closed, observe the sky at approximately 45 degrees angle. Repeat steps **a.** and **b.** two times. Fig 8-18.

   Note: The waist does not press forward. The buttocks do not scoop backward and the pelvis does not thrust forward. We may see red light after holding the posture a period of time.

   Common mistakes: Chin is not tucked in. Upper body leans backward from the Mingmen instead of fourth thoracic vertebra. Stomach protrudes outward. Coccyx is not pointing downward. Body is not relaxed.

c.   **Closing.** At the end of the repetition, push the head up, straighten the body, and move hands up in a circular motion to above the head. Turn the elbows inward slightly so that the palms face each other. Cup the palms with the wrists at shoulder width. Relax the shoulders and lower the elbows. Lower hands in front of the body, along the face to the chest. Then turn the palms inward and lower the hands along the rib cage until they rest on the waist. Step on qi to close the feet. Fig 8-19 to 8-20.

C. Purpose

The main purpose for opening the front Kua is to loosen up the hip joints and lay down the foundation for sitting meditation. The purpose of opening the back Kua is to loosen up the sacroiliac joint, so that the Dantien area will be enlarged, allowing qi to concentrate in the Dantien area. The Gall Bladder Meridian is located along the outer thighs, while the Bladder Meridian is located along the back of the thighs. By expanding the hip joints out, rotating thighs out and pressing the waist, these two meridians will join in the sacroiliac joint area.

When the knees are relaxed with the big toes turned in and pressed to the ground, the inner thighs relaxed and outer thighs expanded with tension, qi in the foot Shaoyang Gall Bladder Meridian and foot Taiyang Bladder Meridian will be pushed up. When the Baihui is raised, Chingyang qi moves up to nourish the head. When the chin tucks in, qi will move down to Dantien to complete the circle. The back Kua area is usually fixed and immobile. By loosening it, the tailbone will gradually be able to move and to turn. Opening the front and back Kuas can also strengthen qi in the lower limbs.

IX. Bend Knees to Connect 3 Joints

A. Posture

Following the last movement, squeeze the buttocks inward and move the hip joint (pubic area) forward. Expand the shoulder blades outward and then inward. Hollow the chest, withdraw the abdomen toward Mingmen, and relax the waist. Embrace the elbows inward slightly, push the head up, tuck in the chin, and relax the knees and the ankles. Slowly squat down to the limit. The upper body and the thighs maintain a slanted straight line. Hold this position as long as possible. Push the Baihui forward and upward to straighten the body slowly. Relax the whole body and return to the beginning position. Fig 9-1, 9-2.

Fig 9-1   Fig 9-2

B. Details

1. **Hip movements:** Squeeze the buttocks and wrap them around inward. Raise Huiyin and move back Kua (Sacroiliac joint) forward.

2. **Hollow the chest:** Take a deep breath. Move the shoulders and the first thoracic vertebra up by pulling up the back. Exhale. Drop the shoulders and shoulder blades down toward the back; the shoulders scoop to the front slightly This withdraws the chest. The tips of the shoulders pull outward and upward to expand the chest. Then relax and drop the shoulders to relax the shoulder joints and empty the under-

arms.

3. **Withdraw the abdomen:** The navel looks for and touches Mingmen. Pull up Huiyin.

4. **Squatting-down movement:** With the proper postures (**1.** to **3.**), relax the waist and move the elbows to the front slightly. Pull up Baihui, tuck in the chin, and relax the ankles. Move the knees forward so the thighs and upper body form a slanted straight line. Then squat toward the ground. The knees must pass the toes, and one should visualize them touching the feet. The shoulders lean back past the heels. The lower limbs are united as one unit; the heels must touch the ground at all times. The center of gravity is in the knees.

5. **The head:**

   a. Yintang withdraws into the center of the head, then to Baihui and is pulled up by Baihui.

   b. The tip of the nose looks for the chin, the chin tucks in to the Adam's apple, the Adam's apple to Yuzheng, and then to Baihui. In this way the Dantien qi will be pulled up.

   c. The tip of the nose goes down to Huiyin. Huiyin pulls up the centers of the feet and the knees. Mingmen pulls up Huiyin, and Baihui pulls up Mingmen.

6. **Straighten up movement:** Baihui moves forward and upward to pull up the body. If the knees push up the body instead, loss of balance may occur. When Baihui pulls up with the whole body relaxed, qi will permeate to the feet. The center of gravity shifts back from the knees to the feet.

Common mistakes: The thighs and the body does not form a straight line. Mingmen is pressed inward. Body is not relaxed. Use the legs to push up the body instead of using Baihui to pull up the body.

Keys to the practice

The important part is to contract the buttocks and tip the pelvis forward. The thighs and the body create a straight line by moving the buttocks and coccyx forward. Do not bend the hip joints. Besides the upper limbs, the knees and the ankles, no other joint is allowed to bend. Shift the body's center of gravity to the knees. When in the squat position, use mind intent to pull up the pressure points located in the upper edge of the knee.

Squatting down creates a blockage in the knee area. The longer we hold the position, the more qi will accumulate in the knee and the more uncomfortable we will feel. When the body straightens up slowly leading with Baihui and relaxing the knees, accumulated qi will rush to the feet like water rushing through a broken dam. The rushing qi will gradually open meridians in the lower limbs. The longer and the lower we hold the posture, the stronger the rush will be. Some individuals may feel the qi rushing all the way to the center of the feet or the toes.

C. Purpose

The main purpose of this exercise is to open and loosen up the knees. By opening up the knees, qi will connect the three lower joints (hip joints, knee joints and ankles) and the three sections of the lower limbs will connect as one. This movement is also very effective in treating lower limb joint problems and increasing bone density.

X. Spring leg, move foot to draw Taiji

A. Posture

With the body centered, shift weight to the right, lift the left leg until the thigh is parallel to the ground. The calf is naturally relaxed and pointing to the ground. Flex the toes up, then press down 3 to 5 times. Fig 10-1, 10-2.

Fig 10-1   Fig 10-2

Draw circles with the back of the foot and toes. First draw clockwise then counterclockwise circles 3 to 5 times each. Fig 10-3, 10-3a, 10-4, 10-4a, 10-5, 10-5a, 10-6, 10-6a.

Fig 10-3   Fig 10-4   Fig 10-5   Fig 10-6

Fig 10-3a

Fig 10-4a

Fig 10-5a

Fig 10-6a

Straighten the back of the foot, then spring the foot out at 45 degrees to the left front, leg forming a straight line. Flex toes up and push heel out. Then point toes downward. Fig 10-7, 10-8. Repeat 3-5 times.

Straighten the back side of the foot; then turn the toes inward and draw circles, first clockwise and then counterclockwise. Fig 10-3 to 10-6. Repeat 3 to 5 times.

Fig 10-7   Fig 10-8

Withdraw big toe inward and move the leg back to the beginning position. Fig 10-9.

Repeat the same movements with the right leg. Fig 10-1 to 10-9.

Fig 10-9

B. Details

1. **Move leg movement:** Shift weight to the right. Lift left leg, heel moving up first, followed by the toes until the thigh is parallel to the ground. The calf is relaxed and naturally pointing to the ground. The body will become substantial on the right side and insubstantial on the left. Keep the body centered, attention on the center of the left foot. Fig 10-1 to 10-2.

   Keys: In order to maintain balance, we have to relax the mind. Once the mind tenses, the body will not be able to relax. The pelvis sits down slightly. Relax the body by taking a deep breath and exhale to sink qi into Dantien. If we cannot hold the thigh parallel to the ground, we can lower the foot or touch the heel to the ground.

2. **Flex and press foot and rotate ankle movement:**

   Flex: The back of the foot pulls up and back to the limit first, then the toes pull up and back to the limit.
   Press: The ankle and then bottom of the foot press down to the limit first. The toes then point downward. Repeat **Flex** and **Press** 3 to 5 times.
   Rotating ankle: Rotate the toes to the left, down, right, and up 3 to 5 times. Repeat the rotation in the opposite direction 3 to 5 times. Fig 10-3 to 10-6.

   Keys: The flexing and pressing movements must be slow and continuous. The toes rotate as if attached to a silk thread. Movements should be slow and rounded to avoid snapping the silk thread.

3. **Spring out diagonally:** Straighten the back of the foot and spring it out diagonally at 45-degrees to the left front. The leg forms a straight line naturally. At the final position, the thigh should open 45-degrees to the side and lift to a 45-degree angle off the ground.

   Keys: Do not turn the foot and then spring out. It should spring out at 45 degrees. Do not turn the body after the foot is sprung out. The body should remain centered. Do not thrust the pelvis forward; it should be withdrawn slightly.

4. **Flex, stretch, and press foot and rotate ankle movement:**

   Flex: Pull the back of the foot up to the limit first; then pull the toes up to the limit.
   Stretch: Stretch the heel forward to the limit.
   Press: Press down the ankle and bottom of the foot to the limit first; then point the toes downward. Repeat **Flex**, **Stretch**, and **Press** 3 to 5 times.

Rotating ankle: Rotate the toes to the left, down, right, and up 3 to 5 times. Repeat the rotation in the opposite direction 3 to 5 times. Fig 10-7 to 10-8.

Keys: When the heel stretches, the leg remains straight. The rest is the same as **1**.

Common mistakes: Body is not centered, either leaning toward back and/or to the side. Movements are not performed to the limit. Circles are not circular or even.

C. Purpose

In the previous nine sections, we concentrate on the upper body. As a result, qi becomes more concentrated in the upper body. This imbalance will sometimes create an uncomfortable feeling in the head. By moving the feet, the qi sinks down and becomes more balanced. By focusing on the toe movements, we can effectively activate the Foot Meridians.

The combination movements of toes and legs activate the 6 meridians (3 Foot Yang and 3 Foot Yin). Pulling the big toe inward while withdrawing the foot can activate the Liver Meridian and the Spleen Meridian. Cupping the center of the foot can activate the Kidney Meridian. Rotating the ankles can activate the Yuan Pressure points of 6 feet Meridians located in the ankle area. Spring leg and flex foot can activate the Yangming Stomach Meridians located in the front of the thigh. Stretch and press movements can activate the foot Taiyang Bladder Meridians located in the back of the thigh. These movements are very effective in treating problems in the joints, muscles and ligaments of the lower limb and in regulating blood pressure.

XI. Return Qi to One

A. Posture

1. Wan Yuan (blend internal qi) to one

Following the last movement, relax and separate the hands. Turn hands until the thumbs point to the front and the tiger mouth (opening formed by the thumb and the rest of the fingers) points upward. The palms are slightly cupped and facing each other at shoulder width and slightly below the waist. Fig 11-1.

Fig 11-1

Extend arms forward and downward diagonally, and then scoop qi up with the hands as if holding a qi ball to above and in front of the head. Turn the body to the left. Fig 11-2, 11-3.

Fig 11-2   Fig 11-3

Relax the whole body, drop the shoulders, sink the elbows, and squat
down. During the squat, the arms draw a downward arch from the left side
to the front. Keep the body centered during the squat. Do not push the
buttocks backward. As the body reaches the lowest point in the squat, the
arms should arrive in front of the body with the hands in front of the knees.
Relax the wrists and the fingers, allowing the fingers to point to the
ground. Fig 11-4, 11-5.

Fig 11-4   Fig 11-5

Turn body to the right. The
shoulders, elbows and wrists
slightly lift up. The hands draw
an upward arch until the hands
arrive above and in front of the
head as the body raises up from
the squat. This would complete a
full circle. Fig 11-6, 11-7. Repeat
11-2 to 11-7 three times

Fig 11-6

With the same principles, draw three circles in the reverse direction.

At the end of the last circle, move hands to above the head and stay there. Perform 3 Crane's Neck movements in the forward direction (see Fig 2-1 to 2-8 for details). Fig 11-7, 11-8, 11-9, 11-10.

Fig 11-7

Fig 11-8

Fig 11-9

Fig 11-10

2. Blend internal and external qi to one

Lower the hands as if pulling the qi ball to cover the head: move the wrists down and in toward each other followed by the palms and fingers (the hands do not touch each other). Relax the shoulders, lead with the elbows to lower and open the hands from both sides until the tips of the middle finger are next to the tip of the ears, the hands and forearms forming a diagonal straight line. Fig 11-11 to 11-15.

Fig 11-11

Fig 11-12

Fig 11-13

Fig 11-14

110

Fig 11-15   Fig 11-16

Then move the hands upward along the same path, closing first, then opening, as in the letter "X". Fig 11-16 to 11-19.

Repeat three times (Fig 11-11 to 11-19).

Fig 11-17   Fig 11-18

Scoop the qi up with the hands and pour qi into the head. Relax shoulders and lower the hands in front of the face to the chest; rotate the palms inward until the fingers are pointing to each other. Lower hands to the abdomen. Rotate palms until the fingers are pointing to the ground and continue moving downward in front of the legs to the feet. Fig 11-20, 11-21, 11-22.

Fig 11-19

Fig 11-20

Fig 11-21

Fig 11-22

Put hands on top of the feet with fingers on top of the toes. Press the hands downward and move the knees forward and down. Through mind intent, the hands go through the feet to connect with the earth. Then the hips move up and the knees shift back and up. The mind intent is to collect earth qi into the body. Fig 11-23, 11-24, 11-25, 11-26. Repeat 3 times.

Fig 11-23

Fig 11-24

Fig 11-25

Fig 11-26

Separate hands from the feet and move hands slightly upward. Cup the palms, rotate and move the hands until the palms are facing the inner legs. Move the hands upward along the inner legs to the abdomen. Turn hands until the fingers are pointing toward each other. Fig 11-27, 11-28.

Fig 11-27   Fig 11-28

Separate hands to the sides. Leading with the little fingers, rotate palms forward and place in front of the shoulders. Push the right hand forward until the arm is almost straight. Fig 11-29, 11-30.

Fig 11-29   Fig 11-30

Relax wrist and turn palm to scoop qi to the left, turning the body at the waist. At 90 degrees, the tip of the thumb touches Zhongkui (middle of the middle joint of middle finger). Bend the elbow and circle the hand around the shoulder to continue scooping qi. At the same time, the body begins to return to the beginning position. Return arm to front of the left chest and press Qihu (under the collar bone) with the tip of the third finger. Fig 11-31, 11-32, 11-33.

Fig 11-31

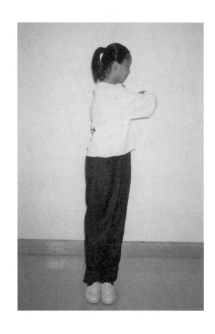

Fig 11-32

Fig 11-33

Fig 11-34

Repeat the same movement with the left hand. At the end of the movement, the forearms should cross each other forming an "X" in front of the chest. The upper arms should form a 45-degree angle with the body with the elbows pointing downward diagonally. Breathe in and out 3 times naturally. When inhaling, the middle fingers press Qihu slightly. When exhaling, release the pressure and pronounce the word "Tong" soundlessly. Fig 11-34, 11-35, 11-36.

Fig 11-35

Fig 11-36

Fig 11-37

Release fingers and push forearms forward to form a 90-degree angle with the upper arms. With the wrists touching each other, turn palms to face the sky and rotate wrists to form a lotus palm. Close hands in praying position. Fig 11-37, 11-38, 11-39.

116

Fig 11-38   Fig 11-39

3. Closing

From the praying position, open hands to the nipple line. Then close hands until almost touching. Open and close the hands 3 times.Fig 11-40,11-41.

Fig 11-40   Fig 11-41

Move the hands to the tip of the nose. Open and close 3 times. Fig 3-42, 11-43, 11-44.

Fig 11-42

Fig 11-43

Fig 11-44

Fig 11-45

118

Move hands to Yintang. Open and close 3 times. Fig 11-45, 11-46, 11-47.

Fig 11-46

Fig 11-47

Then move hands to Xingmen. Open and close 3 times. Fig 11-48, 11-49, 11-50.

Fig 11-48

Fig 11-49

Fig 11-50   Fig 11-51

Finally move hands to above Baihui. Open and close 3 times. Fig 11-51, 11-52, 11-53.

Fig 11-52   Fig 11-53

Close hands and move them upward until the arms are straight, then stretch farther. Separate hands and turn palms forward. Fig 11-54, 11-55.

Fig 11-54   Fig 11-55

Lower the arms to form a straight line at shoulder level. Turn palms up to face the sky. Fig 11-56

Fig 11-56

Move arms forward to shoulder width. Withdraw the palms and arms slightly; middle fingers bend slightly to deliver qi to Yintang. Withdraw the elbows backward and outward until middle fingers touch Dabao and deliver qi inside. Move hands to the back until arms are almost straight, then circle hands to the sides. Fig 11-57, 11-58, 11-59, 11-60.

Fig 11-57   Fig 11-58

Fig 11-59   Fig 11-60

Turn palms to scoop qi forward and into the Dantien. Close hands in front of the navel (approximately one finger's thickness). The man puts the left hand first and the woman, the right hand first. Massage counterclockwise (left, up, right and down) 9 times from small to large, then clockwise 9 times from large to small. Put the hands upon the navel and relax for a few minutes. Slowly return hands to the beginning position and open eyes. Fig 11-61, 11-62, 11-63, 11-64.

Fig 11-61

Fig 11-62

Fig 11-63

Fig 11-64

B. Details

1. Wan yuan (blend internal qi) to one

a. Hold the ball to draw circles

i. **Holding the ball.** Release hands to hold a ball in front of the abdomen. The arms are at shoulder width and the hands are holding an imaginary qi ball. While rotating the body, the distance between the hands should remain constant. Maintain the feeling of holding a ball, not emptiness. When raising the ball up in front of the body, the shoulders move the elbows and the elbows move the hands. The qi between the hands and the qi inside the body should be connected. Fig 11-1.

ii. **Rotating the body to draw circles.** Relax the whole body, drop the shoulders, sink the elbows and sit the wrists. The arms draw a downward arch from the left side. At the same time, the body turns to the left using the waist and sits down. The hands move down while holding the ball. The body remains straight and centered. When the hands are in front of the knees, relax the wrists and the fingers. The fingers will automatically point to the ground. Turn the body to the right. When moving upward, slightly raise the shoulder blades, using the shoulders to lead the elbows and the wrists to move upward slowly. From the right side of the body, the hands draw an arch up to above the forehead. Repeat the movement 3 times. Reverse the direction. At the end of the last circle, the hands stop above the head. Fig 11-2 to 11-7.

Common mistakes: The ball becomes big and small. The ball is not in front of the body. The shoulder leans forward too much. The hip is not sitting down. The waist is not turning.

Keys to the practice

In order to acquire a feel for the movement, we can practice either **i.** or **ii.** independently. Once the movements become familiar, **i** and **ii** should be performed simultaneously. Holding the ball and turning the body are whole body movements. Both upper and lower limbs and the body are turning and drawing circles. Joints must be relaxed, the movements are natural and harmonized, and the body and limbs should move as one. The body and arm movements should be synchronized and natural.

In order to let the arms draw better circles, the body can lean slightly backward when turning. The mind intent should focus on connecting the ball to the body. While turning, imagine the ball is touching the body and connecting with the qi ball inside the body.

Purpose

The focal points of the Body and Mind method are different in each section. Consequently, the qi and the qi flow in the body becomes uneven. This sequence of movements balances and blends internal body qi into one by moving every part of the body simultaneously.

b. Crane's Neck

After the last movement, move hands to above the head and perform three Crane's Neck movements. The principles are the same as in section II except the movement is smaller. The purpose for this movement is to induce qi to the head for preparation to open the Tienmen (Heaven's Gate). Fig 11-8 to 11-10.

2. Blend internal and external qi to one

a. Opening the top

The movements are down, close, open, up, close, open. The hands pull a qi ball downward to cover the head to open the Tienmen (Heaven's Gate).

Down: The palms close downward diagonally, starting with the wrists and followed by the palms and fingers. Fig 11-11 to 11-12.

Close: The wrists close, then open. The palms close, then open. The fingertips close, then open. The hands almost touch, but do not touch during the closing. Fig 11-13.

Open: Relax the shoulders. Leading with the elbows, move hands down diagonally from the sides until the tips of the middle fingers arrive next to the tips of the ears. Hands and forearms form a straight line. Fig 11-14.

Reverse the path when performing the up, close and open movements. When going up, close first, then open, as if drawing an "X" over the top of the head. When the palms and the fingers open above the head, visualize the Tienmen opening. The distance between the wrists above the head should not be wider than the dragon's horns. The whole movement looks like a blossoming lotus flower. Repeat this movement 3 times. Fig 11-15 to 11-18.

Common mistakes: Hands open too big. Not forming an "X". Elbows do not open to the sides.

b. Inducing qi

After the last movement, hands scoop qi upward, as if holding a ball, and pour qi into the head. Relax the shoulders and sink the elbows. Lower the hands along the face to the chest, then turn palms inward until the fingers point to one other. At the abdomen, slowly turn the fingers downward and lower hands along the front of the legs until the center of the palms rest on top of the feet with the fingers resting on top of the toes. Press hands down and move the knees slightly forward and downward. Through mind intent, centers of the palms pass through the centers of the feet to touch the ground. Then move hips upward, and shift the knees backward and upward slightly. Visualize pulling earth qi into the body. Press down and up three times. Fig 11-19 to 11-26.

Move the hands upward and above the feet slightly. Then cup the palms and turn the fingers outward 90 degrees in opposite directions. Lift the wrists slightly so the palms are facing each other and the fingers are pointing to the ground. The hands next to the outside edge of the feet pull up earth qi and hold it between the hands. Circle the hands around the feet. Turn palms to face the inner leg and move up. When the hands pass the abdomen, turn the palms inward until fingers point toward one other and move to the chest level. Separate hands by sitting the elbows and turn palms forward leading with the little fingers until the palms are in front of the shoulders. Fig 11-27 to 11-29.

Common mistakes: In press up and down movement, flexing the legs instead of using the Mingmen to press down and pull up. Chin is not tucked in. While straightening up the body, tailbone is not tucked in.

c. Blending qi to one

Sit the right wrist and push the right hand forward until the arm is almost straight. Relax wrist and turn hand to face the left leading with the little finger. Using the waist, turn the body to the left. At the same time, right hand scoops qi to the left. At 90 degrees, the tip of the thumb presses Zhongkui as the rest of the fingers curve naturally. Bend elbow and circle hand around the shoulder to scoop qi. At this time, the body begins to turn right, returning to the beginning position. With continuous turning of the body, the hand should have gone around the shoulder to drop below the lower edge of the collar bone by the time the body is back to the beginning position. Then, the middle finger presses Qihu (middle of the collar bone below its lower edge). Repeat the movement with left hand. Fig 11-30 to 11-36.

Common mistakes: The waist is not turning. The tip of thumb does not press Zhongkui.

d. Breathing and Sounding "Tong"

By this time, the forearms are crossing each other forming an "X" in front of the chest. The upper arms point downward diagonally forming a 45-degree angle with the body. Inhale and exhale naturally 3 times. When inhaling, tips of the middle fingers press Qihu. Release the pressure while exhaling, and at the same time pronounce the word "Tong" silently. Then, release the fingers and push the forearms forward to form a 90-degree angle with the upper arms (which remain stationary). Lower the fingers to turn palms to face the sky. Rotate the wrists outward in opposite directions until the hands and the forearms form an "X", a "lotus palm". Put hands together and lower hands to form praying position in front of the chest. Fig 11-36 to 11-39.

Common mistakes: The breathing is not natural but forced. The tips of thumb are not touching Zhongkui. Upper arms do not form a 45-degree angle with the body. Sounding the word "Tong" loudly.

Purpose: During qigong practice, a strong qi field forms around the body. Scooping this condensed outside qi into the body and blending it with the inner qi is called "returning the qi". The purpose for saying "Tong" is to induce qi upward to push open Tienmen. Before pronouncing "Tong", the tongue must touch the upper palate to induce qi upward.

3. Closing

a. Five open-close movements

The open-close movement requires the elbows and shoulders to move simultaneously and the hands and forearms to be fixed at a 90-degree angle throughout the movements. When the forearms maintain a straight line, the elbows lead the hands to do the open-close movement. These are not hand movements. When closing, the hands are almost touching yet not touching. After practicing for a certain period of time, we will feel the opening and the closing of the inner organs and the head. This occurs because the open-close movement is not isolated but a whole-body-qi open-and-close movement. Fig 11-40 to 11-53.

i. **Tanzhong (the midpoint between the nipples) open-close.** The hands open to the nipples, with the second knuckles of the thumbs at Tanzhong level.

ii. **Tip of the nose open-close.** Hands open to the cheek bones with the tips of the thumbs at nose tip level.

iii. **Yintang open-close.** Hands open to the center of the pupils with the first knuckle of the thumbs at the Yintang level.

iv. **Xingmen (about two cm above the forehead) open-close.** Hands open to the center of the pupils with the whole thumbs inclined toward Xingmen.

v. **Baihui open-close.** Hands open to the dragon's horns with the fingers pointing to the sky and the wrists ten cm above Baihui.

Common mistakes: Forearms do not form a straight line. Openning too wide.

Purpose: The open-close movements blend the internal and external qi together. It lays the foundation for practicing stillness qigong.

b. The closing

Put hands together and move them up along the body center line to above the head. When the arms are straight, hands stretch upward to the maximum to induce Chingyang Qi and Shuyang Qi upward. Rotate the arms until palms are facing the front, then lower arms to shoulder level to form a straight line. Rotate arms until palms face up toward the sky. Circle arms inward and forward to shoulder width. Slightly bend the first knuckle of the middle fingers to reflect qi into Yintang. Fig 11-54 to 11-58.

Holding a qi ball in the hand, lower and withdraw the elbows to the back until hands touch the rib cage. Then rotate elbows outward until tips of the middle finger touch Dabao. Slightly press Dabao to deliver qi inside. Continue rotating the elbows until the fingers are pointing backward. Extend arms to the back forming a straight line with the hands holding a qi ball at Mingmen level. Circle arms to the side and naturally rotate arms to scoop qi to the front and deliver it into the Dantien through the navel. Slowly close hands in front of the navel to approximately one finger's thickness away from the abdomen. Men place the left hand down first with right hand overlapping the left hand. Women place the right hand first. Draw nine circles from small to large. Then reverse the direction and draw nine circles from large to small. Put the hands on the navel and nourish qi for a few minutes. When the hands draw circles, mind intent is inside the abdomen and turning with the hands. Fig 11-59 to 11-63.

Purpose. The closing collects universal qi into the body and blends it with the body qi.

Part 2:
Tap along the Meridians

Introduction

Tap along the meridians is a very important part of Body & Mind Method. Its main function is to strengthen meridians' lateral abilities. One tap is one pressing and one pulling. As indicated in the name, this method uses tapping technique to tap along the meridians to achieve the lateral opening results. It does not tap along one meridian at a time. It taps along either the three Yin or three Yang meridians.

The routines for the twelve meridians are as follow:

Hand Yin Meridians run from the chest to the hands along the inner arms,
Hand Yang Meridians run from the hands to the head along the outer arms.
Foot Yang Meridians run from the head to feet along the back.
    Note: Yangming (Stomach) Meridian runs in the front and is not tapped.
Foot Yin Meridians run feet to stomach along the inner legs.

The directions for tapping are:

Hand Meridians:
Downward: Tap along the inner arm.
Upward: Tap along the outer arm.
Foot Meridians:
Downward: Tap along the back of the body.
Upward: Tap along the inner legs and front of the body.

I. Opening

Same as Body and Mind Method.

II. Tap along the Hand Meridians

From praying hand position, step on qi and separate feet to shoulder width. Separate hands from the waist, turn left palm facing the sky and extend left hand forward at 45-degree angle. At the same time, right hand moves up along the rib cage, passes Qimeh, Tanzhong and to the left Yunmen. Right hand taps down along inner left arm, along Quze, Daling, Laogong to the fingertips. Fig 12-1, 12-2, 12-3, 12-4, 12-5.

Fig 12-1

Fig 12-2

Fig 12-3

Fig 12-4

Fig 12-5

Turn left palm down and move to right fingertips. Left palm taps up along the outer right arm, passes Waiguan, Quichi, Binao, and Jianyu to the base of the right neck. Mind intent moves upward to the head. Fig 12-6, 12-7, 12-8.

Fig 12-6 Fig 12-7 Fig 12-8

Left palm moves down to the right Yunmen. At the same time, turn right palm to face the sky. Left palm taps down along inner right arm, passes Quze, Daling, Laogong to the fingertips. Fig 12-9, 12-10, 12-11.

Fig 12-9 Fig 12-10 Fig 12-11

Turn right palm over and place on left fingertips. Right palm taps up along the outer left arm, passes Waiguan, Quichi, Binao, and Jianyu to the base of the left neck. Mind intent moves upward to the head.
Fig 12-12, 12-13, 12-14.

Fig 12-12 Fig 12-13 Fig 12-14

Right hand moves down, passing collar bone, Yunmen, Tanzhong, Qimeh to rest on waist. At the same time, withdraw left hand to the right side, across the abdomen, and rest on the waist. Fig 12-15, 12-16.

Fig 12-15   Fig 12-16   Fig 12-17

Separate the hands from the waist, turn right palm up to face the sky and extend right hand forward at 45-degree angle. At the same time, left hand moves up along the rib cage, passing Qimeh, Tanzhong and to the right Yunmen. Fig 12-17, 12-9.
Left hand taps down along inner right arm, along Quze, Daling, Laogong to the fingertips. Fig 12-9, 12-10, 12-11.

Turn right palm down and move to left fingertips. Right palm taps up along the outer left arm, passes Waiguan, Quichi, Binao, and Jianyu to the base of the left neck. Mind intent moves upward to the head.
Fig 12-12, 12-13, 12-14.

Right palm moves down to the left Yunmen. At the same time, turn left palm up to face the sky. Right palm taps down along inner left arm, passes Quze, Daling, Laogong to the fingertips. Fig 12-3, 12-4, 12-5.

Turn left palm down and move to right fingertips. Left palm taps up along the outer right arm, passes Waiguan, Quichi, Binao, and Jianyu to the base of the right neck. Mind intent moves upward to the head. Fig 12-6. 12-7, 12-8.

Left hand moves down, passing collarbone, Yunmen, Tanzhong, Qimeh to rest on waist. At the same time, withdraw right hand to the left side , across the stomach, and rest on the waist. Fig 12-17, 12-16.

III. Tap along the Foot Meridians

Turn palms inward and upward along the ribcage until middle fingers touching each other. Palms tap up along the chest, neck, chin and face. Fig 12-18, 12-19, 12-20.

Fig 12-18   Fig 12-19   Fig 12-20

Gradually turn fingers upward, to forehead, Yanmen, Baihui and Yuzhen. Fig 12-21, 12-22, 12-23.

Fig 12-21   Fig 12-22   Fig 12-23

Palms cover the ears. Fingers hit Yuzhen to vibrate the lower brain in sequence. This is called "Sound the Heaven's Drum". Fig 12-24, 12-25, 12-26.

Fig 12-24   Fig 12-25   Fig 12-26

Continue to tap down along the neck until arms cannot go farther. Stop tapping and circle hands around the shoulder and underams. Then, move hands up along the back and with mind intent connecting the path, resume tapping down. Fig 12-27, 12-28, 12-29.

Fig 12-27   Fig 12-29   Fig 12-30

Body curls downward, gradually bending knees. After hands pass Huan-tiao, thumbs stay on the outer side of the legs while the rest of fingers move to back side of legs. Continue tapping down along the outside of the feet until fingers tap the toes. Fig 12-31, 12-32, 12-33, 12-34.

Fig 12-31   Fig 12-32   Fig 12-33

Continue to tap along the inner feet, inner leg, stomach and chest. At the same time, gradually straighten up the body. Repeat the same movement twice. Fig 12-35, 12-36, 12-37, 12-38.

Fig 12-34   Fig 12-35   Fig 12-36

Fig 12-37   Fig 12-38

Note: Three repetitions of tapping along the hands and feet constitutes one circle.

IV. Closing

After the last repetition of patting along the feet, close hands in a praying position. Step on qi and close feet. Move hands up until the arms are straight, then stretch farther. Separate hands and turn palms forward. Lower arms to form a straight line at shoulder level. Turn palms up to face the sky. Fig 12-39, 12-40, 12-41.

Fig 12-39

Fig 12-40

Fig 11-56

Move arms forward to shoulder width. Withdraw the palms and arms slightly; the middle fingers reflect qi to Yintang. Move elbows backward and outward until the middle fingers touch Dabao and deliver qi inside. Move hands back to the limit and circle hands to the sides. Fig 12-41, 12-42, 12-43, 12-44.

Fig 12-41

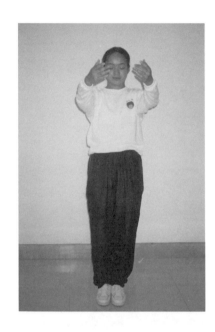

Fig 12-42

Fig 12-43

Fig 12-44

Turn palms to scoop qi forward and into the Dantien. Put hands upon the navel. Man puts the left hand down first and woman, the right hand down first. Relax for a few minutes. Slowly return hands to the beginning position and open eyes. Fig 12-45, 12-46, 12-47, 12-48.

Fig 12-45   Fig 12-46

Fig 12-47   Fig 12-48

Keys to the practice:

Switching hand: When switching hands, the movement should be smooth and rounded. For example, when right palm taps to tip of left hand, left hand extends out to the right slightly in a circular motion, at the same time, right hand moves backward to the left in a circular motion. Then turn hand naturally.

Sound the Heaven's Drum: Palms cover the ears. Fingers hit Yuzhen to vibrate the lower brain in the following order: index fingers hit once, ring fingers hit once, and middle fingers hit once. Then all three fingers hit together three times.

Tapping technique: In the beginning, hands should touch the skin at all times. Once the technique is mastered, separate hands from skin about 1 to 3 cm. The speed should be about 2 times per second. From the shoulder to the fingertips and back to shoulder takes about 10 cycles of natural breaths. From head to toes about 24 cycles of natural breaths. When the hand touches the skin, visualize the hand pressing into center of the bone. When the hand leaves the skin, visualize the hand pulling out from the center of the bone.

Purpose

In Lift Chi Up and Pour Chi Down Method (Level 1 of Chi-Lel™ Qigong), external Wan Yuan qi is exchanged with internal qi at the level of the skin. The main purpose of Body and Mind Method (Level 2 of Chi-Lel™ Qigong) is to cultivate the exchange of external Wan Yuan qi with internal qi at the cellular level. Even though meridian qi is strengthened by this method, qi tends to pool in localized areas. The tapping technique is used to pull qi in and out of the tissues in a direction perpendicular to the meridians to further refine the body's ability to exchange internal and external qi as well as to distribute localized qi more evenly throughout the body to enhance health.

C. Pressure Point Diagram

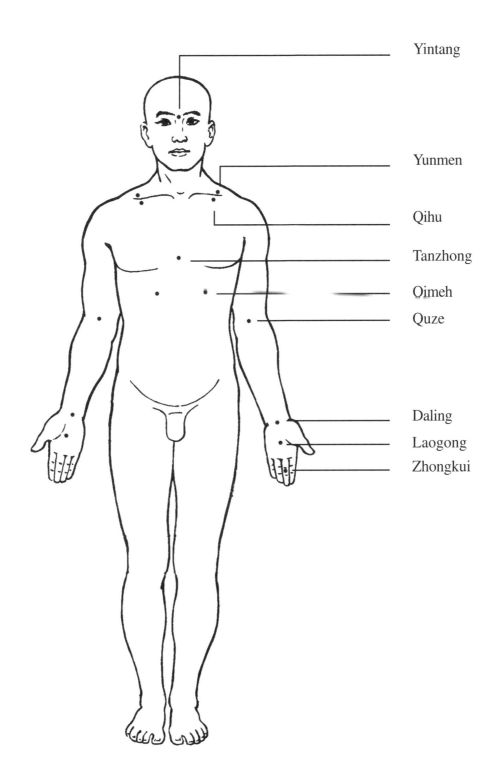

Yintang

Yunmen

Qihu

Tanzhong

Oimeh

Quze

Daling

Laogong

Zhongkui

Pressure Point Diagram

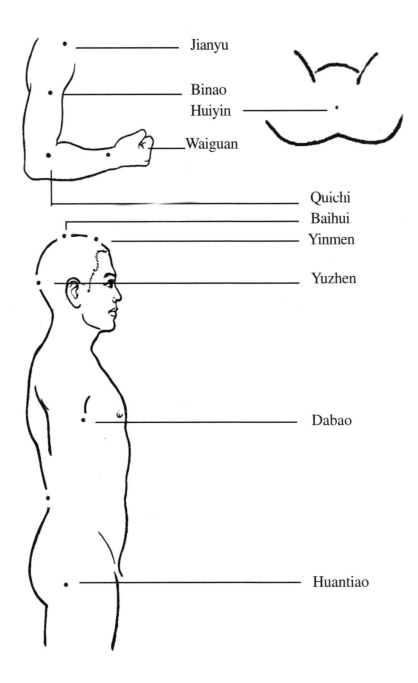

Jianyu

Binao

Huiyin

Waiguan

Quichi

Baihui

Yinmen

Yuzhen

Dabao

Huantiao

Accompanying Videotape and Audio CD

Video

with Master Luke Chan

This videotape contains demonstration of the method and step-by-step instructions. You will learn the ten sequence described in this book.

> Crane's Neck and Dragon's Horns
> Squeeze Shoulder Blades and Shrink Neck
> Erect Palms, Separate Fingers to Open Meridians
> Yi Qi Thrust
> Bend Body, Arch Back to Loosen Dumein
> Turn Waist, Move Kua
> Open Front and Back Kua
> Kneeling on Top of Feet to Connect 3 Joints
> Spring Leg, Flex Foot to Draw Taiji
> Return Chi to One

Running time: 83 minutes

Audio CDs
Body & Mind Method:

Disc 1:	Boby & Mind Method fast versoin (33 Min) Boby & Mind Method slower versoin (45 Min)
Disc 2:	Crane's Neck and Dragon's Horn Gong Spring Leg, Flex Foot Gong
Disc 3:	Squeeze Shoulder Blades and Shrink Neck Gong Turn Waist Move Kwa Gong
Disc 4:	Bend Body Arch Back Gong Yi Qi Thrust Gong

Chi-Lel™ Qigong Products

Videotapes

101 Miracles of Natural Healing
With Master Luke Chan

This videotape offers 103 Minutes of :
Step-by-step instructions for-
1. Lift Chi Up and Pour Chi Down Method
2. 3-Centers Merge Standing Method
3. La Chi
4. Wall Squatting

Actual footage from China of-
1. Bladder cancer removed in real time using qi
2. Testimonials of recovered patients
3. Group practice of Chi-Lel™
4. Fa Chi- emitting qi for healing

Advanced Level 1 of Chi-Lel™ Qigong
with Master Luke Chan

This video complements the 101 Miracles video with focus on:
How to do the movements correctly
What to visualize while doing the form
How to organize the Chi-Field
How to do the wall squatting using Mingmen

For Taiji video, visit our website at:

www.chilel.com

Book

by Master Luke Chan

Inspirational stories of 101 individuals who miraculously recovered from cancer, diabetes, arthritis, paralysis, heart disease, and many other chronic illnesses. The natural healing method they used was developed by Dr. Pang Ming and employed in the Huaxia Zhineng Qigong Center, which has treated more than 135,000 patients with over 180 different diseases. The self-healing art is easy to follow. It is for all age groups.

Audio CDs

Level 1, Practice Series

Disc 1:   Lift Chi Up and Pour Chi Down Method
3-Centers Merge Standing Method
LCUPCD and 3-C Combination

Disc 2:   6-Directions La Chi
Journey to Health and Happiness La Chi

Disc 3:   Push and Pull Gong
Wall Squatting Gong
Press Up and Down Gong

Disc 4:   Full Moon Practice: Lift Chi Up and Pour Chi Down with Fa Chi

For latest teaching aids and qigong products, visit our website at:

www.chilel.com

Chi-Lel Activities

Study in China

Friendship

Practice at Sedona

Healing Circle

Relaxing

End of Workshop

For China Trip and Workshop/Retreat information, visit our website at:
www.chilel.com or call 1 (888) 864-0588.